MATH YOU REALLY NEED

ROBERT GARDNER and EDWARD A. SHORE

 P A A C
Foundation   "Together we will build a better future."

The addition of this resource to the
John M. Cuelenaere Public Library
was made possible by the Prince Albert &
Area Community Foundation
2008 Literacy Grant.

 WALCH PUBLISHING®

User's Guide
to
Walch Reproducible Books

As part of our general effort to provide educational materials which are as practical and economical as possible, we have designated this publication a "reproducible book." The designation means that purchase of the book includes purchase of the right to limited reproduction of all pages on which this symbol appears:

Here is the basic Walch policy: We grant to individual purchasers of this book the right to make sufficient copies of reproducible pages for use by all students of a single teacher. This permission is limited to a single teacher, and does not apply to entire schools or school systems, so institutions purchasing the book should pass the permission on to a single teacher. Copying of the book or its parts for resale is prohibited.

Any questions regarding this policy or requests to purchase further reproduction rights should be addressed to:

Permissions Editor
J. Weston Walch, Publisher
P. O. Box 658
Portland, Maine 04104-0658

1   2   3   4   5   6   7   8   9   10

ISBN 0-8251-2799-8

Copyright © 1996
J. Weston Walch, Publisher
P. O. Box 658 • Portland, Maine 04104-0658

Printed in the United States of America

Contents

Introduction .... *v*

Additional Instructional Material .... *vi*

Skill-Builder 1: Conversions .... *vii*

*Skill-Builder 2: Powers of Ten and
    Scientific Notation* .... *xii*

Skill-Builder 3: Significant Figures .... *xv*

Chapter 1 **Baseball**

Teacher Section and Answers 1

Reproducible Student Section 6–15

   1. What's My Batting Average? 6

   2. Slugging Averages 8

   3. Earned-Run, Fielding, On-Base, and Stealing Averages 10

   4. Hank Aaron and Babe Ruth: A Comparison of
        Home-Run Production 12

   5. Baseball Geometry 14

Chapter 2 **Traveling**

Teacher Section and Answers 17

Reproducible Student Section 29–51

   6. Speed, Time, and Distance 29

   7. Change, Cambio, Wechsel: Changing Foreign Currency 32

   8. MPG, the EPA, and the Cost of Driving 34

   9. Buying a Car 40

  10. Avoiding Rear-End and Multiple-Car Collisions 41

  11. What Time Is It? 45

  12. Temperature Scales 49

Chapter 3 **Music and Art**

Teacher Section and Answers 53

Reproducible Student Section 58–67

  13. The Mathematics of Music 58

  14. Musical Scales 62

  15. Math in Art 65

Chapter 4 **Money**

Teacher Section and Answers 69

Reproducible Student Section 81–96

   16. Paying the Electric Bill 81

   17. Budgets 82

   18. Business and Graphs: Line and Bar Graphs 83

   19. Business and Graphs: Pie Graphs 87

   20. Paying for a College Education 89

   21. Buying Land 91

   22. How Money Grows! 93

   23. Plan Ahead: Saving for Retirement 97

Chapter 5 **Around the House**

Teacher Section and Answers 99

Reproducible Student Section 108–123

   24. Using Math in Cooking 108

   25. Painting the House 111

   26. Degree-Days, Fuel, and Heating Costs 113

   27. The Usable Energy from Household Lightbulbs 117

   28. Lumber and Board Feet 119

Chapter 6 **Math in Many Places**

Teacher Section and Answers 125

Reproducible Student Section 133–145

   29. Estimation and Approximation:
       How Many Stars in the Night Sky? 133

   30. Estimation and Approximation:
       Approximating Distance 135

   31. Estimation and Approximation:
       Sampling Red Blood Cells 136

   32. Flagpole Math 139

   33. How Wide Is the River? 140

   34. Rising Seas 142

   35. Statistics, Lies, and Murders 143

Introduction

Our goal in writing this book was to introduce a variety of real-world situations that would serve as a source of questions for students. We wanted to show how mathematics can be used to solve problems that students may or will encounter in their own lives.

At the same time, we were constantly guided by the standards recommended by the National Council of Teachers of Mathematics. As a result, you will find that much of the material in this book fosters the ideas and suggestions found in *Curriculum and Evaluation Standards for School Mathematics* (1989) recommended by the working groups of the Commission on Standards for School Mathematics of the National Council of Teachers of Mathematics (NCTM, 1906 Association Drive, Reston, VA, 22070). In particular, we have used "problem solving as a means as well as a goal of instruction," as recommended in the *Standards*. We have certainly tried to encourage the active involvement of students in making use of mathematics, we have suggested a variety of approaches ranging from individual investigations to whole-class activities where information is shared, we have encouraged students to communicate ideas through discussion and writing as well as by calculations, and we have assumed that students will make use of pocket calculators and perhaps have access to calculators or computers with graphing capabilities as well.

By choosing problems from a variety of sources, we believe students will recognize the connections between mathematics and other disciplines. Generally, students recognize that mathematics is a valuable tool for the scientist and engineer, but they may not be aware of the role of mathematics in sports, travel, music, art, money, household activities such as cooking and buying paint and lumber, making everyday estimates, and so on.

The questions throughout the book are designed to make use of real-world problems. We hope to motivate students to apply theory to concrete situations. Further motivation will come from doing the analyses required by the problems, comparing solutions, and questioning one another as to whether the answers seem reasonable.

As you can see from the Contents, we have chosen as our sources baseball, travel, the arts, activities related to the household, money, and a variety of other uses of mathematics in everyday life or in answering interesting questions. As former teachers, we know how difficult it is to find time to write questions or develop problem situations that will both challenge and motivate students. We hope you will find that many of these problems meet your needs, are appropriate for your students, and will help them to see that mathematics can play a significant role in their lives.

Additional Instructional Material

Although we recognize the value of unit analysis in problems that require conversion of units, the propitious use of scientific notation in dealing with large and small numbers, and the importance of the proper use of significant figures in calculations based on measurements, we believe that these ideas are best introduced when a need for them arises. Furthermore, we believe these ideas are best handled by the individual teacher who knows when his or her students are ready to deal with these useful concepts. We also realize that a busy teacher often does not have time to prepare questions that would give students practice in converting units, making use of scientific notation, or knowing how many significant figures are appropriate. Consequently, we have included the following "skill-builders" to provide support and practice problems for your students when and if you decide to introduce these concepts. You will find references to these skill-builders in the "To the Teacher" material at the beginning of each chapter.

Skill-Builder 1: Conversions

Although most scientists and many others would prefer to see the metric system adopted in the United States as it is in most of the rest of the world, the reality we face daily is the need to use different units for the same dimensions and to convert units within and between systems. Since you will be using the technique of unit or dimensional analysis in some of the problems found in this book, a number of additional practice problems are given below.

In addition to learning how to use unit analysis in solving problems, you will be using some of the fundamental units of length, area, and volume involved in the solution of many practical problems.

Unit analysis, essentially, involves multiplying by one. A fraction such as 3 feet/ 1 yard is really another way of writing 1, because 3 feet = 1 yard. The same is true of conversions from one system of measurement to another. For example, multiplying a value by the fraction 39.37 inches/1.0 meter is the same as multiplying by 1, because 39.37 inches = 1.0 meter.

Life would certainly be a lot easier if our society could agree on one system of measurement. Scientists use the metric system most of the time in their work. But once outside their laboratories, they, too, deal with a world made more complicated than necessary by multiple systems of measurement. Highway signs give distances to towns and cities in both miles and kilometers; speedometers record our rate of motion in mph and kph; we buy milk in pint, quart, half-gallon, and gallon containers, soda in 1-liter and 2-liter bottles or 12-ounce cans; we buy wood by the cord, lumber by the board foot, and land by the acre; but in most of the world, wood is sold by the cubic meter and land by the hectare.

Because we face more than one system of measurement on a daily basis, we must be prepared to convert measurements from one system to another or to other units within the same system—ounces to pounds, meters to kilometers, inches to yards, kilograms to grams, and so on. Although there is no substitute for knowing the various units within a system and the conversion factors needed to change from one system of measurement to another, it is possible to use the units in a method known as unit analysis so that the conversion process becomes quite simple.

Suppose that you want to convert a distance given in feet to the same distance in miles. Since there are 5,280 feet (ft) in a mile (mi), the conversion factor is 5,280 ft/mi. Thus, if it is 1,500 ft from your house to your school, the distance in miles is:

$$1{,}500 \text{ ft} \times \frac{1.0 \text{ mi}}{5{,}280 \text{ ft}} = 0.285 \text{ mi.}$$

By writing the conversion factor in the form 1.0 mile divided by 5,280 feet, you are, in effect, multiplying 1,500 ft by 1.0, because 1.0 mile and 5,280 feet are equal. However, by so doing, the units of feet cancel out. Just as 4/4 = 1 or 9/9 = 1, so ft/ft = 1.

(continued)

Skill-Builder 1: Conversions *(continued)*

You might like to show this by writing the equation with a strike-through line drawn across the foot unit in both the numerator and denominator:

$$1,500 \ \cancel{ft} \times \frac{1.0 \ mi}{5,280 \ \cancel{ft}} = 0.285 \ mi.$$

Similarly, if you wish to convert a distance in miles to the same distance in feet, you write the conversion factor so that the units in miles cancel because they appear in both numerator and denominator. For example, if the distance from your home to that of a friend is 1.3 miles, the distance measured in feet is:

$$1.3 \ \cancel{mi} \times \frac{5,280 \ ft}{1 \ \cancel{mi}} = 6,864 \ ft.$$

Sometimes it is necessary to make more than one conversion in solving a problem. Suppose that you want to find the weight of a concrete slab that was poured on a flat roof because you are afraid it may not be safe. The contractor tells you that the slab is 12 feet by 10 feet and is 4 inches thick. In a handbook of science you find that the density of concrete is 2,900 kg/m^3; that is, each cubic meter of concrete weighs 2,900 kilograms.

To convert the density in kilograms per cubic meter to pounds per cubic foot, you need to know that a kilogram is equivalent to 2.2 pounds (lb) and that there are 3.28 feet in a meter. You first determine the number of cubic feet in a cubic meter:

$$3.28 \ ft/m \times 3.28 \ ft/m \times 3.28 \ ft/m = 35.3 \ ft^3/m^3.$$

Knowing that 35.3 cubic feet is equivalent to 1.0 cubic meter, you can now convert the density in kg/m^3 to lb/ft^3 by using the English system equivalents for kilograms (2.2 lb) and cubic meters (35.3 ft^3):

$$\frac{2,900 \ \cancel{kg}}{1.0 \ \cancel{m^3}} \times \frac{2.2 \ lb}{1.0 \ \cancel{kg}} \times \frac{1.0 \ \cancel{m^3}}{35.3 \ ft^3} = 181 \ lb/ft^3.$$

Now, you can calculate the weight of the concrete:

$$\frac{181 \ lb}{1.0 \ \cancel{ft^3}} \times 12 \ \cancel{ft} \times 10 \ \cancel{ft} \times \tfrac{1}{3} \ \cancel{ft} = 7,240 \ lb,$$

$$\text{or } 7,240 \ \cancel{lb} \times \frac{1.0 \ ton}{2,000 \ \cancel{lb}} = 3.62 \ tons.$$

Table 1 lists a number of conversion factors within and between English and metric systems of measurement that you will find helpful in solving problems.

(continued)

Skill-Builder 1: Conversions (continued)

Table 1: Conversions Within and Between English and Metric Systems of Measurement

Length Within English	Length Within Metric	Length, English to Metric
5,280 ft = 1 mi = 320 rods	1 km = 1,000 m	1.0 mi = 1.6 km
16.5 ft = 1.0 rod = 5.5 yd	1,000 mm = 100 cm = 1.0 m	1.0 in = 2.54 cm = 25.4 mm
36 in = 3.0 ft = 1.0 yd		39.37 in = 3.28 ft = 1.00 m

Area Within English	Area Within Metric	Area, English to Metric
43,560 ft^2 = 1.0 acre = 160 rod^2	10,000 m^2 = 1.0 hectare	1 acre = 0.405 hectare
		2.471 acres = 1.0 hectare

Volume Within English	Volume Within Metric	Volume, English to Metric
16 oz = 1 pt = 0.5 qt	1,000 cm^3 = 1,000 mL = 1.0 L	1 qt = 0.946 L = 946 mL
4 qt = 1 gal = 231 in^3		1 gal = 3.785 L

Additional Practice Problems

1. While driving through Germany, you see a road sign in Hamburg indicating that the distance to Berlin is 290 kilometers (km). Because your car has an odometer that records distance in miles, you wish to know the distance in miles so that you can gauge your position as you travel between these two cities. What is the driving distance between Hamburg and Berlin in miles?

2. During the trip, you stop for gas. After filling the tank, the gauge on the gasoline pump reads 45 L (liters). The cost, in American dollars, is $41.00. In order to keep accurate and complete records, you decide to answer the following questions:

   a. How many gallons of gasoline are equivalent to 45 L?

   b. What was the price of the gasoline in dollars per gallon?

3. You measure the inside dimensions of a fish tank and find that it is 12 inches wide, 1.5 feet long, and 12 inches deep.

   a. How many gallons of water will it take to fill the tank?

(continued)

Skill-Builder 1: Conversions *(continued)*

   b. What are the dimensions of the tank in centimeters?

   c. What is the volume of the tank in cubic centimeters (cm^3)?

   d. How many liters of water will it take to fill the tank?

4. You decide to use a 1.0 L soda bottle as a measuring device. You buy a liter of your favorite soda. Before you drink the liquid, you mark the level of the liquid in the bottle so you will have a mark for one liter. A friend suggests that since a liter is larger than a quart, you might use the same bottle to measure quarts and pints as well as liters. You take your measuring bottle to school and borrow a 100 mL graduated cylinder so that you can add marks to the bottle that will indicate a pint and a quart of liquid.

   a. How many milliliters (mL) of water should you add to the bottle in order to add a mark that will indicate one pint?

   b. How many milliliters (mL) of water should you add to the bottle in order to add a mark that will indicate one quart?

   c. You decide to make marks to indicate fluid ounces as well. How many milliliters of water should you add for each ounce line?

   d. How many ounce lines should be on the bottle by the time you reach the 1.0 qt line?

   e. If the bottle is filled to the 1.0-L mark, how many ounces will you have to pour out before the liquid reaches the 1.0-qt line?

5. How would you build a cubic box that would hold exactly:

   a. 1.0 liter?

   b. 1.0 gallon?

Math You Really Need

Skill-Builder 1: Conversions

Answers

1. $290 \ \cancel{km} \times \dfrac{1.0 \text{ mi}}{1.6 \ \cancel{km}} = 181 \text{ mi}$

2. a. $\dfrac{1.0 \text{ gal}}{3.785 \ \cancel{L}} \times 45 \ \cancel{L} = 11.9 \text{ gal}$

   b. $41.00/11.9 \text{ gal} = 3.45/\text{gal}$

3. a. $12 \text{ in} \times 12 \text{ in} \times 18 \text{ in} = 2{,}592 \text{ in}^3; 2{,}592 \text{ in}^3/ \ 231 \text{ in}^3/\text{gal} = 11.2 \text{ gal}$

   b. $12 \text{ in} \times 2.54 \text{ cm/in} = 30.48 \text{ cm}; 18 \text{ in} \times 2.54 \text{ cm/in} = 45.72 \text{ cm};$ therefore, the dimensions are $30.48 \text{ cm} \times 30.48 \text{ cm} \times 45.72 \text{ cm}$

   c. Volume $= 30.48 \text{ cm} \times 30.48 \text{ cm} \times 45.72 \text{ cm} = 42{,}500 \text{ cm}^3$

   d. $42{,}500 \text{ cm}^3/1{,}000 \text{ cm}^3/\text{L} = 42.5 \text{ L}$

4. a. $\dfrac{946 \text{ mL}}{1.0 \ \cancel{qt}} \times \dfrac{1.0 \ \cancel{qt}}{2 \text{ pt}} = 473 \text{ mL}$

   b. 946 mL

   c. $\dfrac{1.0 \ \cancel{pt}}{16 \text{ oz}} \times \dfrac{473 \text{ mL}}{1.0 \ \cancel{pt}} = 29.6 \text{ mL/oz}$ or approximately 30 mL should be added each time a new ounce line is added.

   d. 32 lines, since a quart contains 32 ounces

   e. $\dfrac{32 \text{ oz}}{1.0 \ \cancel{qt}} \times \dfrac{1.0 \ \cancel{qt}}{0.946 \text{ L}} = 33.8 \text{ oz/L}; 33.8 \text{ oz} - 32.0 \text{ oz} = 1.8 \text{ oz}$ that will be poured out in going from a volume of 1.0 liter to 1.0 quart

5. a. Since $1.0 \text{ L} = 1{,}000 \text{ cm}^3$, you would build a cube with sides equal to the cube root of $1{,}000 \text{ cm}^3$, or $(1{,}000 \text{ cm}^3)^{1/3} = 10 \text{ cm}$. So the inside dimensions of the cube would be 10 cm on each side. Another solution would be to take the log of $1{,}000$, which is 3, divide by 3, and take the antilog, which is 10.

   b. Since a gallon is equivalent to 231 in^3, the cube root of 231 in^3 will give the length of the cube into which a gallon will just fit: $(231)^{1/3} = 6.14 \text{ in}$. Again, an alternative solution is to use logarithms: $\log 231 = 2.36; \frac{1}{3} \times 2.36 = 0.788$; antilog of $0.788 = 6.14$.

Skill-Builder 2:
Powers of Ten and Scientific Notation

Expressing numbers in scientific notation eliminates the need to write lots of zeros when dealing with very large or very small numbers. Numbers such as 10, 100, 1,000, 10,000, 100,000, and 1,000,000 can be written as $10^1, 10^2, 10^3, 10^4, 10^5, 10^6$, that is, as powers of ten, because $10^1 = 10$ (one 10), $10^2 = 10 \times 10$ (two 10's multiplied), $10^3 = 10 \times 10 \times 10$ (three 10's multiplied), $10^4 = 10 \times 10 \times 10 \times 10$ (four 10's multiplied), and so on.

If we multiply numbers written as powers of ten, we can simply add the exponents to find the product. For example, $10^2 \times 10^2 = 10^4$ ($100 \times 100 = 10,000$), or $10^3 \times 10^4 = 10^7$ ($1,000 \times 10,000 = 10,000,000$). If we divide numbers written as powers of ten, we can find the dividend by simply subtracting the exponent in the denominator from the exponent in the numerator. Thus, $\frac{10^2}{10^1} = \frac{10 \times 10}{10} = \frac{100}{10} = 10^1 = 10$ (any number raised to the first power is the number itself—e.g., $2^1 = 2, 5^1 = 5, 9^1 = 9$, etc.), $\frac{10^6}{10^2} = \frac{1,000,000}{100} = 10^4$, $\frac{10^2}{10^2} = \frac{10 \times 10}{10 \times 10} = \frac{100}{100} = 10^0 = 1$ (any number raised to the zero power is 1, hence, $2^0 = 1, 5^0 = 1, 8^0 = 1$, and so on).

If we divide 10^2 by 10^3, the answer, according to our rule, must be 10^{-1} because $2 - 3 = -1$. The explanation becomes clear if you look at the following sequence of numbers, each one tenth as large as the previous one, and the corresponding power of ten written beneath the number.

10,000	1,000	100	10	1	0.1	0.01	0.001	0.0001 …
10^4	10^3	10^2	10^1	10^0	10^{-1}	10^{-2}	10^{-3}	10^{-4} …

Thus, $\frac{10^3}{10^7} = 10^{-4}$ and $\frac{10^2}{10^{19}} = 10^{-17}$.

Any number can be written as the product of a number between 1 and 10 (called the coefficient of the power of ten) and a power of ten. For example, 150 can be written as 1.5×10^2, 32,000 as 3.2×10^4, 56,000,000 as 5.6×10^7, 0.0150 as 1.5×10^{-2}, 0.00032 as 3.2×10^{-4}, and so on. Numbers written in this manner are said to be written in scientific notation.

The product of two numbers written in scientific notation can be found by multiplying their coefficients and then adding their powers of ten. For example:

$$3.0 \times 10^6 \text{ m} \times 4.0 \times 10^5 \text{ m} = 12 \times 10^{11} \text{ m}^2 = 1.2 \times 10^{12} \text{ m}^2.$$

(continued)

Math You Really Need

Skill-Builder 2: Powers of Ten and
Scientific Notation *(continued)*

To divide numbers written in scientific notation, find the quotient of the coefficients and then the difference of their powers of ten. For example:

$$2.6 \times 10^4 \text{ m} \div 1.1 \times 10^{22} \text{ m} = 2.4 \times 10^{-18}\text{m}.$$

The following questions will help you to see how useful scientific notation is when dealing with measurements that are very large and very small.

Additional Practice Problems

1. Light travels at a speed of 2.9979×10^5 km/s. How far will light travel in one year?

2. The federal debt is approximately $\$4.5 \times 10^{12}$. The U. S. population is approximately 2.5×10^8 people. What is the national debt in terms of dollars per person?

3. At room temperature, 24 liters of a gas is known to contain 6.0×10^{23} molecules of the gas. How many molecules are there in:

   a. 1.0 L of the gas?

   b. 1.0 mL of the gas?

4. A mole of oleic acid (6.0×10^{23} molecules) weighs 282 g. How much does one molecule of oleic acid weigh?

5. A molecule of oleic acid is about 1.1×10^{-7} cm long and has a cross-sectional area of about 4.6×10^{-15} cm^2. What is the approximate volume of an oleic acid molecule?

6. How many oleic acid molecules would be found in 1 cubic centimeter of the substance?

Skill-Builder 2: Powers of Ten and Scientific Notation

Answers

1. 3.0×10^5 km/s $\times$ 3,600 s/hr $\times$ 24 hr/da $\times$ 365 da/yr $\times$ 1.00 yr = 9.4×10^{12} km

2. $\$4.5 \times 10^{12}/2.5 \times 10^8$ people = $\$1.8 \times 10^4$/person

3. a. 6.0×10^{23} molecules/2.4×10^1 L = 2.5×10^{22} molecules/L

    b. $\dfrac{6.0 \times 10^{23}\,\text{molecules}}{2.4 \times 10^1\ \text{L} \times 1.0 \times 10^3\ \text{mL/L}} = 2.5 \times 10^{19}$ molecules/mL

4. $\dfrac{2.82 \times 10^2\,\text{g}}{6.0 \times 10^{23}\ \text{molecules}} = 4.7 \times 10^{-22}$ g/molecule

5. 1.1×10^{-7} cm $\times 4.6 \times 10^{-15}$ cm^2 = 5.1×10^{-22} cm^3

6. $\dfrac{1.0\ \text{cm}^3}{5.1 \times 10^{-22}\,\text{cm}^3/\text{molecule}} = 2.0 \times 10^{21}$ molecules

Skill-Builder 3: Significant Figures

Suppose you weigh 50.4 mL of water and find that it weighs 50.20 g (grams). To find the density of the water, you divide 50.20 g by 50.4 mL. Your calculator indicates that the quotient of these two numbers is 0.9960317. Can you conclude that on the basis of your measurements you know the density of the sample of water to the nearest ten-millionth of a gram per milliliter?

In measuring anything, you finally come to a point where you have to estimate the number in the measurement. The last number in any recorded measurement is an estimate. It is determined by estimating a point between two lines on a ruler, a telescope, a microscope, a transit, or whatever measuring instrument is being used. Any digit that represents an actual measurement is a significant figure.

Dividing or multiplying two measurements cannot improve the accuracy of the measurements. As a general rule, the number of significant figures in the product or quotient of two or more numbers cannot be greater than the number of significant figures in the least accurate of the measurements. For example:

$$2.3456 \text{ cm} \times 4.1 \text{ cm} = 9.6 \text{ cm}^2, \text{ not } 9.61696 \text{ cm}^2.$$

To see why, remember that the one tenth in 4.1 was an estimate; the measurement could be 4.0 cm or 4.2 cm, since the one tenth was an estimate. So try multiplying 2.3456 by 4.0 and then by 4.2. The results should convince you that the product cannot be more accurate than the less accurate of the two numbers. It is the second digit in the product that is different for the two multiplications:

$$2.3456 \times 4.\mathbf{0} = 9.\mathbf{3}824; \text{ and } 2.3456 \times 4.\mathbf{2} = 9.\mathbf{8}5152.$$

Only the 9 is common to all the measurements. It is in the second digit that the answers begin to differ, which is reasonable, since it was the second figure that was estimated in the original measurement of the less accurate value.

By using scientific notation, the number of significant figures can be clearly expressed. Suppose, for example, that the length of a piece of land is recorded as being 1,206 m long. The measurement tells you that the length was measured to the nearest meter. It is closer to 1,206 m than to 1,205 m or 1,207 m. But you have no way of knowing how many decimeters shorter or greater than 1,206 m it is. To know the measurement with any greater accuracy, you would need an additional significant figure—a more accurate measurement. For example, if the length were written as 1,206.5 m, you would know that it was closer to 1,206.5 m than to 1,206.6 or 1,206.4 m. To obtain the length to the nearest centimeter, you would need still another significant figure, and so on. If the length were written as 1,200 m, you would not know whether the zeros were significant or merely placeholders. By writing the number in scientific notation, that is, as 1.200×10^3 m, you know that both zeros are significant and that the length is known

(continued)

Skill-Builder 3: Significant Figures *(continued)*

to the nearest meter. If it were written as 1.20×10^3 m, you would know that the length is only accurate to the nearest 10 m; it is closer to 1,200 m than to 1,210 m or 1,190 m, but it could well be 1,204 m or 1,196 m. A measurement known only to the nearest 100 m would be written as 1.2×10^3 m, and a measurement that indicates only that the length is closer to one kilometer (1,000 m) than to two kilometers would be expressed as 1×10^3 m. In astronomy, measurements are frequently known only to the nearest power of ten or even less accurately.

The following questions will help you to understand significant figures.

Additional Practice Problems

1. How many significant figures are there in the following measurements?

   a. 12 km

   b. 4.68 mm

   c. 0.468 cm

   d. 0.00468 mm

   e. 3×10^5 light years

   f. 2.503467 km

   g. 20,000 m

   h. 2.00×10^4 m

2. In the question about density raised at the beginning of this section, what is the density of the water to the proper number of significant figures?

3. A concrete step, which is partially buried, is found to be 1.00 m long, 0.30 m wide, and 0.80 m thick.

   a. What is the volume of the concrete step?

   b. The density of concrete is about 2.4×10^3 kg/m^3. How much does the concrete step weigh?

4. The inside dimensions of a fish tank are found to be 30 cm deep, 30.0 cm wide, and 60.5 cm long. What volume of water will the tank hold?

5. The rim of a wheel is found to have a radius of 31.4 cm. What is the circumference of the rim?

Skill-Builder 3: Significant Figures

Answers

1. a. 2   b. 3   c. 3   d. 3   e. 1   f. 7   g. ? Can't determine!   h. 3

2. 50.20 g/50.4 mL = 0.996 g/mL (50.20/50.3 = 0.998; 50.20/50.5 = 0.994)

3. a. 1.00 m × 0.30 m × 0.80 m = 0.24 m^3

   b. 2.4×10^3 kg/m^3 × 2.4×10^{-1} m^3 = 5.8×10^2 kg

4. 30 cm × 30.4 cm × 60.5 cm = 55,000 cm^3 or, better, 5.5×10^4 cm^3

5. $2\pi r = 2\pi \times$ (31.4 cm) = 197.29202 cm = 197 cm (to three significant figures) or, better, 1.97×10^2 cm.

To the Teacher

Students can calculate their own batting averages as well as those of their favorite players. They will also learn how to calculate slugging averages, ERA, fielding averages, and on-base and successful steal averages or percentages. In addition, they can graph and compare the home-run productions and rates of Babe Ruth and Henry Aaron and use their geometry to lay out a baseball field.

1. What's My Batting Average? *(page 6)*

Many youngsters follow baseball very closely. Calculating batting averages is a real-life problem that provides good practice with division and the use of decimals. The best time to use this activity and the next one is during the baseball season or when the World Series is taking place. Students could be asked to calculate their favorite player's average on a daily basis. Can they predict how a 2-for-4 day, a 1-for-3 day, or a 0-for-5 day will affect the player's average?

Answers

1. $192/540 = 0.356$ 2. $159/590 = 0.269$

3. (Ruth) $60/540 = 0.111$; (Maris) $61/590 = 0.103$

4. (Ruth) $540/60 = 9.00$; (Maris) $590/61 = 9.67$

5. $174/470 = 0.370$ 6. $200/551 = 0.363$ 7. $1,556/5,579 = 0.279$

8. $1,568/5,615 = 0.279$ Their team batting averages were the same to three decimal places. The Yankees' average (0.2793) was actually slightly greater than the Blue Jays' average (0.2790).

9. $4,191/11,429 = 0.367$

10. Answers will vary.

2. Slugging Averages *(page 8)*

Calculating slugging averages is more challenging than finding batting averages. Here the total number of bases (singles, doubles, triples, and home runs) must be added before dividing by the number of at-bats. Of course, it is possible for a player to have a slugging average greater than 1.0; but, although it is a frequent occurrence for a major league player to have a day when total bases exceed number of at-bats, such as three doubles in four at-bats, it has never been done by a major league player over an entire season.

Answers

1. No. Even if a player were to get a hit in every at-bat, his or her average would be 1.000.

2. If total bases exceed the number of at-bats, the slugging average will be greater than 1.000.

3. a. $54 + 9 + 36 + 73 = 172$; batting average $= 172/458 = 0.376$

   b. $(54 \times 4) + (9 \times 3) + (36 \times 2) + (73 \times 1) = 216 + 27 + 72 + 73 = 388$; slugging average $= 388/458 = 0.847$

4. a. $181/539 = 0.336$

   b. $365/539 = 0.677$

   c. No. You would need to know how many singles, doubles, and triples he hit, as well as total bases, to calculate how many home runs he hit.

3. *Earned-Run, Fielding, On-Base, and Stealing Averages* (page 10)

Calculating an earned-run average is a bit complicated, because you must first determine the number of nine-inning games that a pitcher has thrown. Fielding averages are also somewhat more difficult than simple batting averages, because they require that you know the total number of chances a fielder has had—put-outs and assists—and how many of these chances were performed successfully—that is, total chances minus errors. On-base and successful steal averages or percentages are easy to calculate but more subtle conceptually.

Answers

1. $\dfrac{67 \text{ ER}}{267 \text{ inn}/9} = 2.26$ ERA, or 267 inn/9 = 29.7 nine-inning games;

   $\dfrac{67 \text{ ER}}{29.7} = 2.26$ ERA

2. a. $25/31 = 0.806$

   b. $192/275.33 = 0.697$

   c. $275\frac{1}{3}$ inn/9 inn game = 30.59 nine-inning games

   ER/30.59 games = 1.14 ERA; ER = 1.14 ERA $\times$ 30.59 games = 34.9

3. $1{,}226/1{,}230 = 0.997$

4. a. Number of chances = 1,276 + 87 + 7 = 1,370; FA = (1,276 + 87)/1,370 = 0.995

   b. 8.7 chances/game × 158 games = 1,374.6 chances; (1,276 + 87)/1,374.6 = 0.992, or 1,374.6 chances − 7 errors = 1,367.6 successful plays/1,374.6 plays = 0.995

   c. The chances per game were determined by dividing 1,370 total chances by 158 games, and 1,370/158 = 8.67, or 8.7 to two significant figures. Because the number was rounded to two figures, you obtain 1,374.6 chances as a product of 8.7 chances/game and 158 games, which makes little sense, because you can't have 0.6 chance. The true fielding average must be based on actual chances and errors.

5. OBA = 260 on-bases/540 at-bats = 0.481

6. SA = 130/165 = 0.788

4. *Hank Aaron and Babe Ruth: A Comparison of Home-Run Production* (page 12)

The NCTM standards recommend that students construct and draw inferences from tables and graphs. That is certainly the main thrust of this exercise, which uses a table of data and graphs to compare the home-run productivity of Hank Aaron and Babe Ruth. In addition, students will probably have to do some research to answer question 3 and some independent thinking to answer question 4.

Answers

1. The graph of Hank Aaron's home-run production has a slope that is almost constant until the last three years of his career. The slope of the Ruth graph, on the other hand, varies much more. There are steady periods, years 8–11 and years 13–18, for example, where the slope is quite constant and steeper than Aaron's graph. The slopes of the graphs measure the rate at which each player hit home runs.

2. a. 714/22 = 32.4 homers/yr

   b. 755/23 = 32.8 homers/yr

   c. The slope in the mid-region of his graph is greater than his average homers per year. The average includes his first year and his last four years, when he hit significantly fewer home runs.

3. Ruth began his career as a pitcher for the Boston Red Sox. As a result, he had relatively few at-bats during his first several years in the majors.

4. The player would have to be a long-ball hitter and enjoy a long career. Both Ruth and Aaron played for more than 20 years. Students may suggest other factors as well, such as a home ballpark that favors their style. Ruth, who was

a left-handed pull hitter, took advantage of the short right-field fence at Yankee Stadium.

5. *Baseball Geometry* (page 14)

Students begin by using their knowledge of geometry to make a scaled drawing of a baseball diamond. They will need paper, compasses, pencils, and rulers.

If possible, have students use the models they have made actually to lay out the base paths on a field. In laying out the real field, students can use spikes and string as a compass and a tape measure to measure 90 feet. Students can find details regarding the positioning of bases, the pitcher's mound, and home plate in a baseball rules book. Alternatively, students can check an actual baseball field to see if the base paths really are at right angles, that the distance from home to second base is the diagonal of a square, that 3-4-5 triangles can be established for intersecting base paths, and that each base path is 90 feet long.

Answers

1. Approaches will vary, but all will need to begin by constructing a perpendicular to a straight line that represents an extended baseline or foul line. The perpendicular line will represent another baseline or foul line. Along each of the perpendicular lines, at points scaled to represent 90 feet from the intersection of the first two lines, additional perpendiculars should be constructed. The intersection of these two perpendicular lines should complete the square. (See Figure T 1-1.)

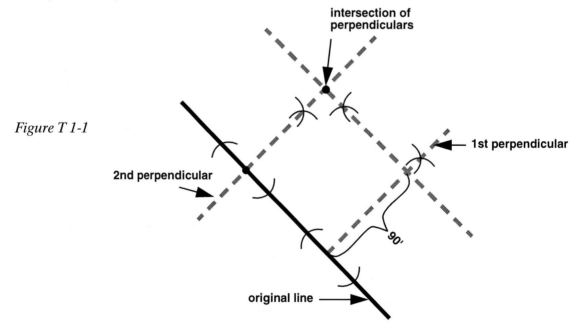

Figure T 1-1

2. The diagonal of a square should equal the square root of the sums of the squares of two sides.

    a. Answers will depend on the scale used. For a scale of 1 cm = 10 ft,
$$D = \sqrt{(9 \text{ cm})^2 + (9 \text{ cm})^2} = 12.73 \text{ cm, or} \cong 13 \text{ cm}$$

    b. $D = \sqrt{90^2 + 90^2} = 127.28$ ft, or $\cong 127$ ft $3\frac{3}{8}$ in

3. Both distances should be 50 feet. If the triangle has a right angle at the intersection of the base paths, the student should have a 3-4-5 (in this case a 30-40-50) triangle.

4.   a. Make a straight line along what is to be the front of the building. Establish perpendicular lines at the points that mark the ends of the building's front. Extend these lines beyond the building's width. At a point along one of these lines, make a mark to show the building's width. Construct a perpendicular at that point and extend it beyond the building's length.

      To be sure the corners are at right angles, measure the diagonal distances between corners and see if 3-4-5 triangles can be formed at each corner.

    b. Figure T 1-2 shows the answer.

Figure T 1-2

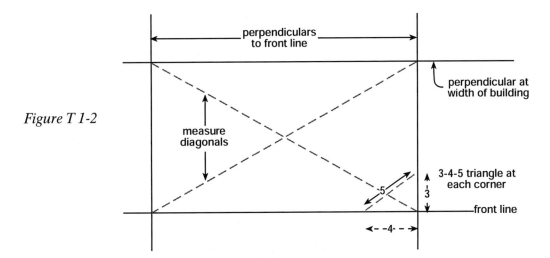

5. Home plate is a right triangle on a rectangle. The area of the rectangle is:
    17.00 in × 8.500 in = 144.5 in².

   The legs of the right triangle have a length given by the Pythagorean theorem:

    $2L^2 = (17.0 \text{ in})^2 = 289 \text{ in}^2; L^2 = \frac{1}{2} (289 \text{ in}^2); L = 12.0 \text{ in.}$

   Thus, the area of the triangle is:

    $\frac{1}{2} bh = \frac{1}{2} \times 12.0 \text{ in} \times 12.0 \text{ in} = 72.0 \text{ in}^2.$

   The total area is 72 in² + 144.5 in² = 216.5 in².

1. What's My Batting Average?

Baseball players are always interested in their batting averages. In fact, a professional player's salary may depend on it. What is a batting average, and how is it determined?

Actually, a batting average is not really an average at all. It is a decimal fraction that shows the ratio of hits to times at bat.

❏ Suppose a major league player has 128 hits in 523 times at bat. His batting average as determined on a pocket calculator is:

$$\frac{\text{hits}}{\text{times at bat}} = \frac{128}{523} = 0.2447419.$$

Since batting averages are usually rounded off to three figures, this player's average would appear in newspapers as 0.245. Because baseball players and fans understand that all batting averages are less than 1.000, the decimal point is sometimes ignored. The player may be said to have a batting average of 245.

❏ Sometimes batting averages are listed under a heading labeled "pct," which is an abbreviation for *percent* (%), which means "per hundred." But batting averages are not expressed as percentages. They are written as a decimal fraction to three places.

1. In 1927, Babe Ruth hit 60 home runs—a record that was not broken until 1961. During the 154-game schedule in 1927, Ruth had 192 hits in 540 times at bat. What was his batting average that year?

2. In 1961, Roger Maris broke Ruth's record. Maris hit 61 four-baggers in a 162-game schedule. During that season, he collected 159 hits in 590 at-bats. What was Maris's batting average in 1961?

3. Compare the home-run records set by Ruth and Maris in terms of home runs per at-bat. Give your answers as decimal fractions.

4. Compare the home-run records set by Ruth and Maris in terms of at-bats per home run.

(continued)

1. What's My Batting Average? *(continued)*

5. The Colorado Rockies entered the National League in 1993. One of their players, Andres Galarraga, was the major league batting champion that year. Galarraga had 174 hits in 470 times at bat. What was his batting average?

6. In the same year, John Olerud of the Toronto Blue Jays was the American League batting champion. Olerud collected 200 hits in 551 at-bats. What was his batting average?

7. As a team, the 1993 Blue Jays had 1,556 hits in a total of 5,579 at-bats. What was the team batting average?

8. The 1993 New York Yankees finished in second place, seven games behind the Toronto Blue Jays. As a team, they collected 1,568 hits in 5,615 at-bats. How did their team batting average compare with the American League champion Blue Jays?

9. Hall of Famer Ty Cobb, who played major league baseball for 24 years, holds the best lifetime career batting average. He had 4,191 hits in a total of 11,429 at-bats. What is Cobb's record-setting career batting average?

10. If you are a baseball player, calculate your current batting average or your batting average from last season. Remember that walks (bases on balls), sacrifice bunts and flies, and the times you were hit by a pitch or reached base because of a fielder's interference do not count as at-bats. Put-outs, errors made on balls you hit, and hits all count as at-bats. As far as batting averages are concerned, any hit—be it a single, double, triple, or home run—counts as one hit.

2. Slugging Averages

Baseball managers and the front-office people who hire players are always interested in long-ball hitters. A long-ball hitter's capability is indicated by a statistic known as slugging average. A player's slugging average is the total bases hit divided by the number of at-bats.

❏ Suppose a player hits a home run, a triple, a double, and a single in 12 times at bat. His or her batting average over these 12 at-bats would be calculated as follows:

$$\frac{4 \text{ hits}}{12 \text{ at-bats}} = 0.333.$$

The player's slugging average could be found by dividing the total bases achieved in these hits by the number of at-bats. In this case:

Type of Hit	Number of bases
home run	4
triple	3
double	2
single	1

Totals: 4 hits   10 bases

$$\text{Slugging average} = \frac{10 \text{ bases}}{12 \text{ at-bats}} = 0.833$$

1. Could a player's batting average ever be greater than 1.000? Why?

2. A player could have a slugging average greater than 1.000. How could this be achieved?

(continued)

2. Slugging Averages (continued)

3. Although slugging averages greater than 1.000 are possible, no major league player has ever achieved one. The record slugging average for a season, as you might guess, is held by Babe Ruth. The record extends back to 1920, when Ruth had 54 home runs, 9 triples, 36 doubles, and 73 singles in 458 at-bats.

    a. What was Ruth's batting average in 1920?

    b. What is Ruth's record-setting slugging average?

4. More recently, in 1993, Barry Bonds of the San Francisco Giants had 365 total bases and 181 hits in 539 at-bats.

    a. What was Bonds's batting average in 1993?

    b. What was his slugging average during the same year?

    c. With the information given, can you tell how many home runs Bonds hit in 1993?

3. Earned-Run, Fielding, On-Base, and Stealing Averages

Baseball is filled with averages. A pitcher's performance is often based on his or her earned-run average (ERA). Any runs scored while a pitcher is on the mound are charged against him or her; however, a run is not counted as an earned run if it is scored by a runner or runners who would have been out were it not for an error committed by one of the pitcher's teammates or by a runner who reached base when batting against another pitcher. A pitcher's ERA is the ratio of earned runs allowed per 9 innings pitched.

Fielders are rated on the basis of their fielding averages. A fielder could have an average of 1.000 if he or she fielded every ball cleanly and made every throw accurately—that is, if the player played errorless ball. Such play is seldom achieved over the course of a long season, but some players have come amazingly close.

Lead-off hitters in particular are evaluated in terms of their on-base averages—the ratio of the number of times they reach base in any way to the number of times they come to bat. The on-base average includes bases on balls, errors by opponents that allow a player to reach base, being hit by a pitch, and so on.

Usually, base-stealing is measured in total bases stolen. But it can be represented as an average (decimal fraction) too. A player who is successful in half of his or her attempted steals has a 0.500 average.

1. In the course of a season, a pitcher allowed 67 earned runs in 267 innings. What was his ERA?

2. In 1909, Hall of Fame pitcher Christy Mathewson won 25 games while losing only 6. He pitched $275\frac{1}{3}$ innings, gave up only 36 walks, allowed only 192 hits, and had an ERA of 1.14.

    a. What was his games-won percentage?

    b. What was his hits-per-inning record?

    c. How many earned runs did he allow?

3. A major league fielder in the course of a season makes only 4 errors in 1,230 chances. What is his fielding average?

(continued)

3. Earned-Run, Fielding, On-Base, and Stealing Averages *(continued)*

4. Don Mattingly, while playing first base for the New York Yankees in 1989, made 1,276 put-outs and 87 assists while committing only 7 errors in 158 games.

    a. What was his fielding average?

    b. His chances (in the field) per game were listed as 8.7. Using that number, what was his fielding average?

    c. Explain why the two fielding averages are not exactly the same.

5. A lead-off batter manages to reach base 260 times in 540 at-bats. What is his on-base average?

6. Rickey Henderson holds the record number of steals in one season, with 130. If he attempted 165 steals, what was his base-stealing average?

4. Hank Aaron and Babe Ruth: A Comparison of Home-Run Production

For many years, Babe Ruth, who retired from baseball in 1935, held the record for most home runs in a career with 714. But in 1974, Hank Aaron moved ahead of Ruth's career record and went on to hit a total of 755 homers, establishing a record that still holds. The table below shows the annual home-run production of each player during his career.

Aaron			Ruth		
Year	Home Runs	Cumulative	Year	Home Runs	Cumulative
1 (1954)	13	13	1 (1914)	0	0
2 (1955)	27	40	2 (1915)	4	4
3 (1956)	26	66	3 (1916)	3	7
4 (1957)	44	110	4 (1917)	2	9
5 (1958)	30	140	5 (1918)	11	20
6 (1959)	39	179	6 (1919)	29	49
7 (1960)	40	219	7 (1920)	54	103
8 (1961)	34	253	8 (1921)	59	162
9 (1962)	45	298	9 (1922)	35	197
10 (1963)	44	342	10 (1923)	41	238
11 (1964)	24	366	11 (1924)	46	284
12 (1965)	32	398	12 (1925)	25	309
13 (1966)	44	442	13 (1926)	47	356
14 (1967)	39	481	14 (1927)	60	416
15 (1968)	29	510	15 (1928)	54	470
16 (1969)	44	554	16 (1929)	46	516
17 (1970)	38	592	17 (1930)	49	565
18 (1971)	47	639	18 (1931)	46	611
19 (1972)	34	673	19 (1932)	41	652
20 (1973)	40	713	20 (1933)	34	686
21 (1974)	20	733	21 (1934)	22	708
22 (1975)	12	745	22 (1935)	6	714
23 (1976)	10	755			

(continued)

4. Hank Aaron and Babe Ruth: A Comparison
of Home-Run Production *(continued)*

1. Use the data given in the table to plot a graph (use your graphing calculator if you have one) of each player's cumulative home-run production during his career. Plot cumulative home runs on the vertical axis and year (1, 2, 3, ...) on the horizontal axis. You may plot both sets of data on the same pair of axes if you wish. Compare the graphs for the two players. What do you notice? What do the slopes of these graphs measure?

2. a. What was Ruth's average home-run production per year?

   b. What was Aaron's average home-run production per year?

   c. How does Aaron's average home-run production per year compare with the slope of the mid-region of his graph?

3. How can you explain Ruth's slow start as a home-run hitter?

4. Based on the information you have seen and graphed, what type of player might break Aaron's career record for home runs?

5. Baseball Geometry

The infield of a baseball field is called a diamond. It is really a square in which the 90-foot-long base paths form the perimeter of the figure. In this section, you are asked to prepare a model for laying out a baseball field. Then, if the space is available, you can actually mark out the lines needed on a flat field.

1. With pencil and paper, prepare a model of how you would go about laying out a baseball field.

2. To check your construction of the square, measure the distance from the intersection of the first and third baselines to the intersection of the baselines that extend from first to second and third to second. What should that distance be:

   a. on your scaled drawing?

   b. on an actual field?

3. Here is another way to check the construction of the square diamond. Start from the point where the baseline between home plate and first base meets the baseline from first base to second base. Measure and mark a distance of 30 feet along the baseline from first base toward home plate. Then measure and mark a distance of 40 feet from first base along the baseline toward second base. Repeat the procedure at third base. (See Figure 1-1.) What should be the distance between points 1 and 2? between points 3 and 4?

Figure 1-1

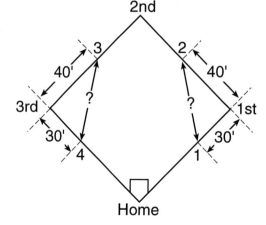

(continued)

5. Baseball Geometry *(continued)*

4. a. How could you use the methods in questions 1, 2, and 3 to lay out and check the outer boundaries of the footings for a building?

    b. Draw a diagram to show how you would lay out the footings.

5. Home plate is a flat, five-sided rubber figure that lies entirely within fair ground. In the early days of the game, it was a square located inside the first- and third-base lines. It was changed to make it easier for both pitcher and umpire to see the plate clearly. It still lies entirely within fair ground, but one half of a 17-inch square has been cut to make this possible, as you can see from Figure 1-2.

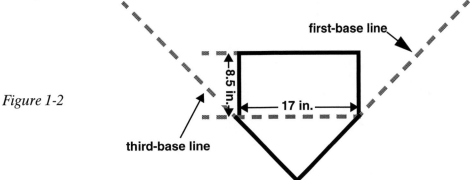

Figure 1-2

What is the area of home plate?

To the Teacher

People who are traveling use math to anticipate arrival times, exchange money, figure out what time it will be when they arrive at their destinations, and convert temperatures and distances to more familiar units. Many who travel use their automobile. Such people use mathematics when buying a car and calculating miles per gallon (mpg), and they can use math to analyze rules they encounter in driver education courses.

6. Speed, Time, and Distance *(page 29)*

In dealing with problems that have units, it is essential to write in the units when solving the problem. For example, the first problem of this section should be written out as follows:

$$\frac{225 \text{ miles}}{4.2 \text{ hour}} = 54 \frac{\text{miles}}{\text{hour}}.$$

In the second problem, it is necessary to change 39 minutes to hours:

$$39 \text{ min} \times \frac{1 \text{ hour}}{60 \text{ min}} = 0.65 \text{ hour. Notice that } \frac{\text{min}}{\text{min}} = 1.$$

In the answers to the questions, each problem is solved with all of the units in place. For additional information and more practice problems on unit analysis, see Skill-Builder 1 on page *vii*.

Answers

1. $\dfrac{225 \text{ miles}}{4.2 \text{ hour}} = 54 \dfrac{\text{miles}}{\text{hour}}$

2. $\dfrac{318 \text{ mi}}{2.65 \text{ hr}} = 120 \text{ mi/hr}$

3. $227 \text{ mi} \times \dfrac{1 \text{ hr}}{120 \text{ mi}} = 1.9 \text{ hours}$

4. $520 \dfrac{\text{mi}}{\text{hr}} \times 4.75 \text{ hr} = 2{,}470 \text{ miles}$

5. $\dfrac{280 \text{ mi}}{3 \text{ hr}} = 93 \text{ mi/hr}$

6. $50 \frac{\text{mi}}{\text{hr}} \times 1.33 \text{ hr} = 67 \text{ miles}$

7. $\frac{393 \text{ mi}}{5.2 \text{ hr}} = 76 \text{ mi/hr}$, well over the posted 65 mi/hr limit

8. $60 \frac{\text{mi}}{\text{hr}} \times 6.75 \text{ hr} = 405 \text{ mi}$. Yes, since you only need to travel 393 miles.

9. The driving time is 7.1 hours $\left(\frac{393 \text{ mi}}{55 \text{ mi/hr}}\right)$. Adding one hour for rest gives a total of 8.1 hours, or 8 hours and 6 minutes.

10. Traveling on Nebraska 2 all the way should take $\frac{274 \text{ mi}}{45 \text{ mi/hr}} = 6.1$ hours, or 6 hours and 6 minutes. The section on U.S. 80 will take $\frac{265 \text{ mi}}{65 \text{ mi/hr}} = 4.1$ hours. Traveling on Nebraska 385 will take $\frac{82 \text{ mi}}{55 \text{ mi/hr}} = 1.5$ hours. This is a total travel time of 5.6 hours, or 5 hours and 36 minutes, a half hour less than the travel time on Nebraska 2.

7. Change, Cambio, Wechsel: Changing Foreign Currency *(page 32)*

In teaching students how to convert from the value of one currency to another, it is important to solve each problem by thinking in terms of the units. This method not only applies to currencies but also is essential in any problem that requires changing from one unit to another. For additional information and student problems regarding the conversion of units, see Skill-Builder 1 on page *vii*.

If you have 1,560 feet that you want to convert to miles, then you can use the fact that there are 5,280 feet per mile:

$$1{,}560 \text{ feet} \times \frac{1 \text{ mile}}{5{,}280 \text{ feet}} = 0.295 \text{ mile}.$$

Notice that the units "feet" cancel, since $\frac{\text{feet}}{\text{feet}} = 1$.

Likewise, to change 1.65 miles to feet:

$$1.65 \text{ mile} \times \frac{5{,}280 \text{ feet}}{\text{mile}} = 8{,}710 \text{ feet}.$$

Depending on what you need to convert, you can use $\frac{1 \text{ mile}}{5{,}280 \text{ feet}}$ or $\frac{5{,}280 \text{ feet}}{\text{mile}}$.

You'll find this method very useful. You can extend the concept to change, for example, 3,400,000 inches to miles:

$$3{,}400{,}000 \text{ inches} \times \frac{1 \text{ foot}}{12 \text{ inches}} \times \frac{1 \text{ mile}}{5{,}280 \text{ feet}} = 53 \text{ miles}.$$

You might like to extend this section by asking students to find the exchange rates for various currencies as if they were planning a trip around the world to various foreign countries. Current rates of exchange for major countries can be found either in the newspaper or at your local bank.

Answers

1. $\$1,000 \times \dfrac{100 \text{ yen}}{\text{dollar}} = 100,000$ yen. 1% of ¥100,000 = ¥1,000, leaving ¥99,000

2. $¥900 \times \dfrac{1 \text{ dollar}}{¥100} = \$9$. 1% of $9 = $0.09, leaving $8.91

3. $\$50 \times \dfrac{1 \text{ peso}}{\$0.302} \approx 165$ pesos

4. A total of L600,000 is required. $\text{L}600,000 \times \dfrac{1 \text{ dollar}}{\text{L}1,505} = \$399$. You will need to exchange four $100 traveler's checks.

5. $\text{L}150,000 \times \dfrac{1 \text{ dollar}}{\text{L}1,505} \times \dfrac{5.45 \text{ francs}}{\text{dollar}} = 543$ francs

8. MPG, the EPA, and the Cost of Driving *(page 34)*

In teaching the first part of this activity, the emphasis must be on using mathematics to *compare* situations. Here we are analyzing the yearly cost of fuel. Although we cannot accurately predict the fuel cost of any particular vehicle, we can compare costs if we set up identical evaluation procedures for all cars. This is good science and a very important application of mathematics. Although this example is simple, the same technique is used in the most sophisticated situations.

For additional class work, here is an example that compares cars with widely different mpg ratings.

❏ Lamborghini Diablo 2-seater, 12-cylinder: city, 9 mpg; highway, 14 mpg.

❏ Honda Del Sol, 2-seater, 4-cylinder: city, 29 mpg; highway, 36 mpg.

Assuming 80% city driving and 20% highway using premium gasoline costing $1.40 per gallon:

15,000 mi/9 mi/gal × $1.40/gal = $2,333

Lamborghini: 0.80 × $2,333 = $1,867

15,000 mi/14 mi/gal × $1.40/gal = $1,500

0.20 × $1,500 = $300

total = $2,167

Honda: 15,000 mi/29 mi/gal × $1.40/gal = $724

0.80 × $724 = $579

15,000 mi/36 mi/gal × $1.40/gal = $583

0.20 × $583 = $116

total = $695

Cost difference: $2,167 − $695 = $1,472

The differences between these two cars are about as extreme as you can get. The Lamborghini, with 12 cylinders, is classified by the EPA as a gas-guzzler. A good class discussion can now evolve around these examples. How important is gas mileage in selecting a car? Consider the cost of fuel; consider the environment.

In the second part of this section, students can actually measure the mpg of a particular car and estimate the cost of owning and operating a motor vehicle. Generally, students believe that fuel is the greatest cost in operating a car, and they tend to underestimate the other costs. Using mathematics, they can make a more reasonable assessment of the cost of automobile ownership while learning how to determine the distance traveled per gallon of fuel as well as some other things every car owner should know.

Answers

1. $15{,}000 \text{ mi} \times \dfrac{1 \text{ gallon}}{19 \text{ mi}} = 789 \text{ gal}$ (highway)

2. $789 \text{ gal} \times \dfrac{\$1.20}{\text{gal}} = \$947$ (highway)

3. $15{,}000 \times \dfrac{1 \text{ gal}}{14 \text{ mi}} \times \dfrac{\$1.20}{\text{gal}} = \$1{,}286$ (city)

4. Since you are driving only half of 15,000 miles on the highway, your cost would be half, or $474. Similarly, the city driving would cost $643. Total cost = $474 + $643 = $1,117.

5. The EPA estimate is less by $1,117 − $1,078 = $39. It is possible that the EPA assumed that the average driver would be putting on more mileage on the highway than in the city.

6. An increase in gasoline cost would give a higher EPA estimate and a higher student estimate. For example, if fuel costs went up 25%, then the EPA estimate would be $1,078 × 1.25 = $1,348. The student estimate would be $1,117 × 1.25 = $1,396. The difference is $48, or $9 more than the estimate for fuel cost at $1.20 a gallon. (Or, easier yet, $39 × 1.25 = $49.)

7. The average is $\dfrac{14 + 19}{2} = 16.5$ mpg.

8. The cost is $15{,}000 \text{ mi} \times \dfrac{1 \text{ gal}}{16.5 \text{ mi}} \times \dfrac{\$1.20}{\text{gal}} = \$1{,}091$. Notice that averaging is *not*

the way to determine fuel costs. You can have the students try a problem where the city driving is 85% and the highway driving is 15%. An averaged value will be quite different from the method outlined here. For example, using the Fleetside Pickup and gasoline at $1.10 per gallon, the tables show:

City driving: $1,179 × 0.85 = $1,002

Highway driving: $868 × 0.15 = $130

Total = $1,132

Averaging gives 16.5 mpg. From the tables, $\$\frac{1031 + 971}{2} = \$1,001$.

9. For the Hyundai, the fuel cost chart shows that 15,000 miles of city driving would cost $917 at $1.10 per gallon. Since only 60% of these miles are actually in the city, $0.60 \times \$917 = \$550$. For the highway, $0.40 \times \$688 = \$275$. The total cost is $\$550 + \$275 = \$825$.

For the Lincoln-Mercury:

City: $0.60 \times \$825 = \$495$

Highway: $0.40 \times \$550 = \$220$

Total = $715

The difference in fuel cost for a year is $\$825 - \$715 = \$110$. This example was chosen from cars that are similarly built. The cost difference is very little.

10. $45968.4 - 45678.9 = 289.5$; $\frac{289.5 \text{ mi}}{10.2 \text{ gal}} = 28.4$ mi/gal

11. a. $\frac{320 \text{ mi}}{12.4 \text{ gal}} = 25.8$ mpg

   b. $34894.9 + 320 = 35214.9$

   c. $35220.0 - 35214.9 = 5.1$ mi

   d. $320.0 + 5.1 = 325.1$; $\frac{325.1 \text{ mi}}{12.4 \text{ gal}} = 26.2$ mpg

12. a. Stop-and-go traffic will give lower mpg values than long trips on the open highway.

   b. Generally, mpg values are higher for summer driving.

   c. Driving over mountains reduces mpg values.

13. During the consumption of a single tankful of gasoline, a car may be driven in unusual circumstances such as heavy traffic or open highways. Further, a calculation involving thousands of miles and many gallons of fuel will give a more accurate estimate of mpg than a single tankful and a couple of hundred miles. The greater distance will cover the car's performance under different driving conditions. Also, failing to fill a tank to capacity by adding 9.5 rather than 10 gallons is an error of 5 percent, which might change a calculation from 31.5 to 30.0 mpg. Over long distances and many gallons, there is no need to be certain the tank is at exactly the same level at consecutive odometer readings.

14. a. $\frac{1,000 \text{ mi}}{25 \text{ mi/gal}} = 40$ gal; 40 gal $\times \$1.25$/gal $= \$50$

   b. $\frac{20,000 \text{ mi}}{5,000 \text{ mi}} = 4$; $4 \times \$30 = \$120$

   c. $20,000$ mi $\times \frac{\$50}{1,000 \text{ mi}} = \$1,000$

d. $1,000 (fuel) + $120 (oil and maintenance) + $1,800 (insurance) = $2,920

e. Answers will vary. Tires and unforeseen parts that may need replacement are possible answers. One major cost that students often neglect is the car's depreciation. If the car was secondhand, cost $5,000, and had an odometer reading of 50,000 miles, it may be prudent to trade it after it has traveled 100,000 miles, which will be 2.5 years later. Assuming it will then be worth $1,500, $3,500 will be needed to purchase a comparable car, assuming no inflation. The car's depreciation is, therefore, approximately:

$$\frac{\$3,500}{2.5 \text{ yr}} = \$1,400/\text{yr.}$$

This brings the car's annual cost to $4,320. Of course, inflation may add to that estimate.

9. Buying a Car *(page 40)*

The main aim of this activity is to show students that when a problem such as buying a car has to be tackled, it is wise to consider only two variables at a time. Once the fuel efficiency problem has been estimated, then other variables can be considered. The next step might be to get at least a ballpark figure for the trade-in values of the cars in two, three, four, or more years. How do these numbers affect the choice of car? Students can consult *Consumer Reports* to get some idea of the probable maintenance cost of each car. A good dealer will have many other suggestions for your students.

10. Avoiding Rear-End and Multiple-Car Collisions *(page 41)*

The NCTM standards emphasize the need for students to be familiar "with informal, but conceptually based, methods for dealing with data and situations involving uncertainty." That is the real message students can acquire from this section. Our data here are crude, but we can still come to some very important conclusions.

This section should appeal to students who are approaching or have reached the age when they may legally drive. The mathematics provides insight into one of the most common causes of accidents—the failure of drivers to allow a safe distance between moving vehicles. The rules presented in driver's education manuals may be part of the reason. The two-second and car-length rules assume that a car traveling twice as fast will travel twice as far as it brakes to a stop. Because reaction time is approximately constant, it is true that the distance a car travels while the driver reacts to a car stopping in front of him or her is proportional to speed. However, as students will learn, braking distance depends on the square of a car's speed, not the speed. Consequently, a driver who uses these rules will not provide a safe distance between cars if the car being followed stops because it collides with a vehicle stalled on the highway.

Tailgating is a very real situation familiar to all of your students. This exercise can be used to give them a practical understanding of how mathematics can alert us all to a situation that we usually deal with intuitively or by using rules that are wrong and can place us in dangerous circumstances.

You'll need to point out to students that the numbers given in this activity are based on assumptions as well as automobile experiments. The reaction time of 0.75 s can easily be much more if the driver has been drinking, has bad vision, is distracted or tired, or is not physically fit. Students should discuss reaction time and its effect on the total distance traveled.

The braking distances are based on experiments performed under controlled conditions. The students can also discuss how this distance would be affected by a slippery road, smooth tires, a drunk driver, and so on.

You might make an additional table giving minimum and maximum estimates to each of the distances—reaction, braking, and total. Then ask the students how their answers to the questions would be altered based on the new estimates.

Answers

1. $\dfrac{1 \text{ mi}}{1 \text{ hr}} \times \dfrac{5{,}280 \text{ ft}}{1 \text{ mi}} \times \dfrac{1 \text{ hr}}{3{,}600 \text{ s}} = 1.47$ ft/s. So 1 mph is equal to 1.47 ft/s.

2.

Speed (mph)	Reaction-Time Distance (ft)
0	0
20	22
40	44
60	66
80	88

3.

Velocity (mph)	Reaction-Time Distance (ft)	Braking Distance (ft)	Total Distance (ft)
0	0	0	0
20	22	20 ± 2	42 ± 2
40	44	72 ± 8	116 ± 8
60	66	180 ± 20	246 ± 20
80	88	376 ± 42	464 ± 42

4.

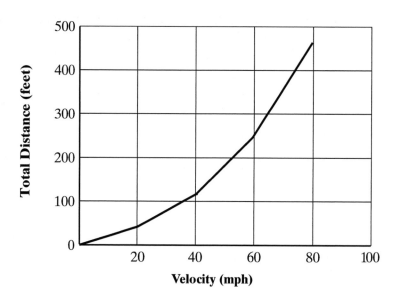

Figure T 2-1

5. Both these rules are highly dependent on traffic conditions, tires, roads, and visibility. Ask your students to discuss these variables. How do they alter the rules? What really is safe driving?

a. If your brakes are as good as the brakes of the car ahead of you and you are traveling at the same speed as that car, both rules should work. As long as you apply your brakes one car length (20 ft) before the place that the car in front of you started braking, there should not be a collision, because you will stop one car length behind the car in front of you.

As the chart below reveals, the distances between cars according to the two-second rule and the car-length rule both exceed the reaction-time distance by more than 16 feet. The only exception is the car-length rule at 20 mph.

Speed (mph)	Reaction-Time Distance (ft)	Two-Second Rule Distance–20 ft	Car-Length Rule Distance–20 ft
0	0	0	0
20	22	29 ft/s × 2 s – 20 ft = 38 ft	40 ft – 20 ft = 20 ft
40	44	59 ft/s × 2 s – 20 ft = 98 ft	80 ft – 20 ft = 60 ft
60	66	88 ft/s × 2 s – 20 ft = 160 ft	120 ft – 20 ft = 100 ft
80	88	120 ft/s × 2 s – 20 ft = 220 ft	160 ft – 20 ft = 140 ft

b. The best we can do is make a first approximation. Remember that this is probably the most important lesson students can learn from this exercise—good math usage does allow us at least to come up with a reasonable answer if we recognize all of the limitations.

Suppose you are driving at 50 mph. The graph shows that you should come to a stop in about 175 feet (between 160 and 200 feet), or 8 to 10 car lengths *under ideal conditions.* The car-length rule at 50 mph suggests that you maintain 5 car lengths in following another vehicle. So this rule does not seem to be a good one. Indeed, many driver's ed books point this out and say that the driver had better learn intuitively that sometimes you may need 20 to 30 (!) car lengths between cars.

The two-second rule is harder to apply. How far are you behind the car you are following at 50 mph? At 50 mph, you will travel:

$$50 \text{ mph} \times 1.47 \text{ ft/s/mph} \times 2 \text{ s} = 147 \text{ ft}$$

in 2.0 s. The rule, therefore, says you should be about 150 ft behind the car in front of you. But this is well below the 175 feet needed to stop. So at this speed, neither rule works.

By plotting the car-separation distances recommended by the two-second rule and the car-length rule on the graph drawn for question 4, students can see that the two-second rule does not work very well beyond about 40 mph, and the car-length rule is useful only at very low speeds.

Figure T 2-2

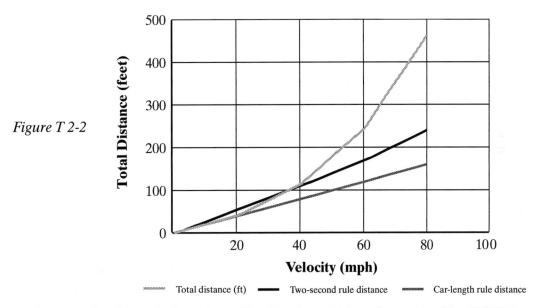

Once again, the main learning will take place during discussion. The NCTM standards recommend that all of your teaching be adjusted to the abilities of your students. This problem is an especially good example of that principle.

6. 5,280 ft/20 spaces = 264 ft/space

7. The car-length rule is 6.5 car lengths, or 6.5 × 20 feet = 130 feet, or about half the distance between reflectors. According to the two-second rule, you should

stay approximately 65 mph × 1.47 ft/s/mph × 2 s = 190 ft. Neither rule is safe, since it will take about 300 feet to bring the car to a stop.

8. Since it is recommended that you be about 130 feet in following, that is about half the distance between reflectors. Be sure to discuss all of the approximations made here, and, of course, reiterate that this rule is not safe.

   If you are actually traveling in a car at 65 mph, or 95 ft/s, you'll find that your estimation of distance is quite inaccurate. The 265 feet between reflectors will appear to most people more like 100 feet. Just from experience, most drivers feel comfortable leaving that spacing between cars, and, on the average, they're not far off.

11. *What Time Is It?* (page 45)

Determining the time in various cities of the world is a good example of numerical thinking. Certain rules must be followed, as outlined in the activity. Then some rigorous numerical thinking must take place. A real map of the time zones is necessary, because the zones are so dependent upon political and economic factors. Yet the underlying principles of physical geography are apparent.

Answers

1. Since there are 360° encircling the globe, the width of each zone is 360°/24 = 15°.

2. The globe, at the equator, is about 24,000 miles in circumference. Therefore, the width of each time zone is 1,000 miles at the equator.

3. The time zones vary widely. At some places a zone can be over 1,000 miles in width; at other places, as narrow as 500 miles. However, you must look at a time zone map of the United States to see how rough this estimate really is. The local variations are due to economic and political preferences. (For students who know basic trigonometric functions, you might ask them to find the circumference of the earth at their latitude, given the earth's radius of 8,000 miles, and then calculate the ideal width of each time zone at your latitude.)

4. The real time zones vary in width because of political and economic reasons. The People's Republic of China, for example, prefers to have the entire country on one time zone, although China really covers five zones. Russia has 11 time zones but advances the hour of all zones by one hour over GMT. The International Date Line does not follow 180° but zigzags around political divisions in the Pacific Ocean. There are many more deviations. Be sure to show your students how the zones vary in the United States, and discuss reasons for these variations.

5. Just west of the dateline we must be into the next day, Monday.

6. After changing to DST, the sun will appear to rise at about 6 A.M.

7. Sunset will occur an hour later when the city changes to DST.

8. When Boston returns to standard time in the fall, sunrise and sunset will both appear to occur one hour earlier.

9.

Place	Time	Place	Equivalent Time
London	5 P.M.	New York	noon
New York	5 P.M.	London	10 P.M.
London	noon Mon	Honolulu	2 A.M. Mon
London	noon Mon	Tokyo	9 P.M. Mon
New York	4 P.M. Sun	Tokyo	6 A.M. Mon
Tokyo	3 P.M. Mon	São Paulo, Brazil	3 A.M. Sun
Chicago	9 A.M.	San Francisco	6 A.M.
Honolulu	9 A.M.	Chicago	1 P.M.
New York	noon (DST)	Seattle (DST)	9 A.M.
New York	noon (DST)	Omaha (STD)	10 A.M.
Manila	1 A.M. (DST) Mon	Cairo (STD)	6 P.M. Sun

12. Temperature Scales *(page 49)*

Medical thermometers are usually calibrated in Fahrenheit degrees. If you can locate one or more medical thermometers (you may be able to borrow medical thermometers from your school nurse), you can have each student take his or her temperature and then convert to °C. A class average can be calculated, but don't be surprised if it is not 37.0 °C. There are many reasons why 37.0 °C (98.6 °F) is not a uniform normal temperature.

Students can check out the freezing point and boiling point of water with thermometers borrowed from the school's science department. For the boiling point, you need only bring some water to the boil, insert the thermometer, and read it when it stops rising. If you have both Celsius and Fahrenheit thermometers, use both at the same time. For the freezing point, freeze some water in ice-cube trays. Then crush the frozen cubes and mix them with some cold water. Allow the mixture to come to equilibrium and then measure the temperature of the ice-water mixture.

You might also have the students collect examples of where the Celsius temperature scale is used.

Answers

1. $\dfrac{180°F}{100°C} = 1.8°F/°C$

2. $30°C \times 1.8\dfrac{°F}{°C} = 54°F$

3. $(54 + 32)°F = 86°F$

4. $\dfrac{100°C}{180°F} = 0.556°C/°F$

5. $(103.5 - 32)°F = 71.5°F$

6. $71.5°F \times \dfrac{0.556°C}{°F} = 39.7°C$

7. $y°C \times 1.8\dfrac{°F}{°C} = °F$ above freezing. Therefore, $y°C \times 1.8\dfrac{°F}{°C} + 32°F = x°F$

   More simply, $1.8C + 32 = F$. Solving for C gives $C = \dfrac{(F - 32)}{1.8}$.

6. Speed, Time, and Distance

Think of yourself in the family car when you were very young, on a trip to see some friends. Do you recall how you were constantly asking, "When will we get there?" Dad or Mom would take a few moments to do a bit of thinking. If you were driving on the interstate and a road sign let you know that there were 63 miles to your destination, then a simple estimate of your arrival time would depend on the average speed that you were able to maintain on the highway. If that speed was estimated to be 60 miles an hour or 60 miles per hour (60 mi/hr), Mom or Dad would tell you that you would arrive in an hour. There doesn't seem to be any math involved in this estimate, but there is. Let's see why.

❑ Suppose your destination is 152 miles away. Assuming no rest stops, and, once again, an average speed of 60 mi/hr, when should you arrive?

You can estimate the answer by figuring that since your speed is 60 mi/hr, you'll cover 120 miles in two hours and 30 additional miles in another half hour. Thus, it will take 2.5 hours to travel:

$$60 + 60 + 30 = 150 \text{ miles.}$$

That's close enough to the 152 miles that you're supposed to go.

You can also solve the same problem by noting that the total distance to be traveled divided by the distance you go in each hour gives the total time of travel. The distance traveled in each hour is the speed. In the case of the car, our destination is 152 miles and our speed is 60 mi/hr. Thus:

$$\frac{\text{distance}}{\text{speed}} = \text{time} = \frac{152 \text{ miles}}{60 \text{ mi/hr}} = 2.5333333 \text{ hours.}$$

You can also write this as $152 \text{ mi} \times \frac{1 \text{ hr}}{60 \text{ mi}} = 2.5333333 \text{ hr.}$

Both $\frac{1 \text{ hr}}{60 \text{ mi}}$ and $\frac{60 \text{ mi}}{1 \text{ hr}}$ are equal to unity. Thus, you can choose which of these fractions is needed for your conversion. The one you want is the one that gives you the answer in the correct unit or units. (Notice that in the expression $152 \text{ mi} \times \frac{1 \text{ hr}}{60 \text{ mi}}$, since $\frac{\text{mi}}{\text{mi}} = 1$, only the unit "hr" remains.)

All those 3's in the answer are there because they showed up on the display of the calculator that was used to perform the division. Let's just drop most of the 3's and say that 2.53 hours is the answer. But even the remaining 3 is not needed. It represents 3 hundredths of an hour, or 1.8 minutes. Since experience has taught us that we can't predict car arrival times to better than a few minutes, 2.5 hours is certainly a reasonable

(continued)

6. Speed, Time, and Distance *(continued)*

answer. It's a good idea always to think about the reasonableness of an answer, isn't it? Here our earlier estimate is the same as our more detailed calculation.

1. What was the average speed of a car that traveled 225 miles in 4.2 hours?

2. The Tokyo to Kyoto "bullet train," the Shinkansen express, travels the 318-mile distance in exactly 2 hours and 39 minutes. It is very regular; you can almost always set your watch by its arrival time. What is the average speed of this train? (You can add the 39 minutes to the 2 hours by first dividing 39 minutes by 60, since there are 60 minutes in an hour. This will give you the total time in hours as 2 + a decimal fraction.)

3. Maintaining this same average speed, how long should the bullet train take to reach Nagoya, a city 227 miles from Tokyo?

4. Just after leaving New York, the pilot of your 747 jet announces that the plane will be traveling at a steady speed of 520 mi/hr and is scheduled to arrive in Los Angeles in 4 hours and 45 minutes. How far will you travel on this New York to Los Angeles flight?

❏ We have seen that the time of travel can always be found by dividing the distance by the average speed.

$$\text{time} = \frac{\text{distance}}{\text{speed}}, \text{ or } t = \frac{d}{s}$$

We also know that the average speed can always be found by dividing the distance by the time.

$$\text{speed} = \frac{\text{distance}}{\text{time}}, \text{ or } s = \frac{d}{t}$$

Have you discovered that the distance can be found by multiplying the speed by the time?

$$\text{distance} = \text{speed} \times \text{time}, \text{ or } d = s \times t$$

All three expressions are really the same:

$$\text{If } t = \frac{d}{s}, \text{ or if } s = \frac{d}{t}, \text{ then } d = s \times t.$$

It's really a practical everyday use of algebra, isn't it?

(continued)

6. Speed, Time, and Distance *(continued)*

Now try some typical problems that arise in everyday travel.

5. What is the average speed of a train that covers a distance of 280 miles in 3 hours?

6. How far will a car travel if it maintains a steady speed of 50 mi/hr for an hour and 20 minutes?

7. You can drive all of the way from Buffalo to New York City on U.S. 90 and U.S. 87, a distance of 393 miles. What average speed must you maintain if you need to be in New York City in 5.2 hours? Can you make this trip without breaking the speed limit?

8. Can the Buffalo to New York City trip be completed if you average 60 mi/hr for 6 hours and 45 minutes?

9. How long will it take to travel from Buffalo to New York City if you average 55 mi/hr while driving and stop for a one-hour rest?

10. In Nebraska there are several ways to go from Grand Island to Alliance. You can travel on Nebraska 2 all the way, a distance of 274 miles, with an average speed of 45 mi/hr. Or, for the first 265 miles, you can travel on U.S. 80, an interstate highway that allows you to maintain an average speed of 65 mi/hr. But U.S. 80 takes you only part of the way. Leaving U.S. 80, you must travel on Nebraska 385 for 82 more miles to reach Alliance. On Nebraska 385, you can maintain an average speed of 55 mi/hr. Which route will take the least time?

7. Change, Cambio, Wechsel: Changing Foreign Currency

Change, Cambio, Wechsel—you'll see these signs all over Europe, wherever there are travelers to be found. If you carry along a simple calculator, you can easily convert monetary values from dollars to foreign currency or foreign currency to dollars.

❏ Suppose the sign in the Paris exchange window lists that, today, U.S. traveler's checks are exchanging at F5.45 (5.45 French francs) for a dollar. This can be written as:

$$\frac{1 \text{ dollar}}{5.45 \text{ francs}} \text{ or as } \frac{5.45 \text{ francs}}{1 \text{ dollar}}.$$

You would like to exchange a $50 traveler's check. How many francs will you receive? Which fraction will you use? If you feel shaky on this decision, first estimate the answer. If you got 5 francs for each dollar, then you would get 250 francs for $50. You must have used the second fraction:

$$\frac{5.45 \text{ francs}}{1 \text{ dollar}} \times 50 \text{ dollars} = 272.5 \text{ francs}.$$

Think of the word *dollar* as canceling. This is the same as:

$$\frac{a}{b} \times b = a, \text{ or } \frac{7a}{b} \times 5b = 35a.$$

The *b*'s cancel. Similarly, $\frac{\text{francs}}{\text{dollar}} \times \text{dollars} = \text{francs}$.

❏ Suppose you saw a sweater in a Parisian shop that was marked at F450. Is this a good buy? You'll have to convert F450 to dollars. You want francs to cancel, so you multiply:

$$\frac{1 \text{ dollar}}{5.45 \text{ francs}} \times 450 \text{ francs} = \$82.56.$$

Now you can make a decision.

Here are some typical situations that you might meet during your travels in other countries.

1. Japanese yen are exchanging at 100 yen to the dollar at Narita airport when you arrive in Japan. How many yen can you expect to receive for a $1,000 traveler's check if a 1% fee is charged for such an exchange?

2. When leaving Narita airport for the United States, you have 900 yen to exchange back into dollars. How much can you expect to receive in U.S. money? The same 1% fee applies.

(continued)

7. Change, Cambio, Wechsel:
Changing Foreign Currency *(continued)*

3. In Mexico City, a sign in a bank window states that the peso is exchanging at $0.302. How many pesos will you receive for a $50 traveler's check?

4. You are planning to spend just 4 days (3 nights) in Italy, staying at the same hotel in Florence. It would be easiest for you to pick up Italian liras when you arrive at the train station in the city, and you hope to have just about none left when you depart. Your room will cost 100,000 liras per night, and you estimate that food will cost L50,000 per day. Adding on another L100,000 for expenses (museums, taxis, etc., plus "unforeseen"), how many $100 traveler's checks should you exchange at the station if the rate of exchange is L1,505 to the dollar?

5. Leaving Italy for France, you find that you have L150,000 in your wallet. How many French francs will you receive at the same rates of exchange as quoted above?

8. MPG, the EPA, and the Cost of Driving

When buying a new car, we usually want to know the number of miles per gallon (mpg) that can be expected from the vehicle. This is one of the cost factors in running the car. For a new car, this information is found on the large label that is attached to the car. The label gives a lot of facts—for example, the standard equipment that comes with the car, the base cost, and the cost of all optional equipment. Very prominently featured is the Gas Mileage Information. Figure 2-1 is a typical label. The vehicle described is a 1995 Fleetside Pickup. The 14 is the city mpg and the 19 is the highway mpg.

Figure 2-1

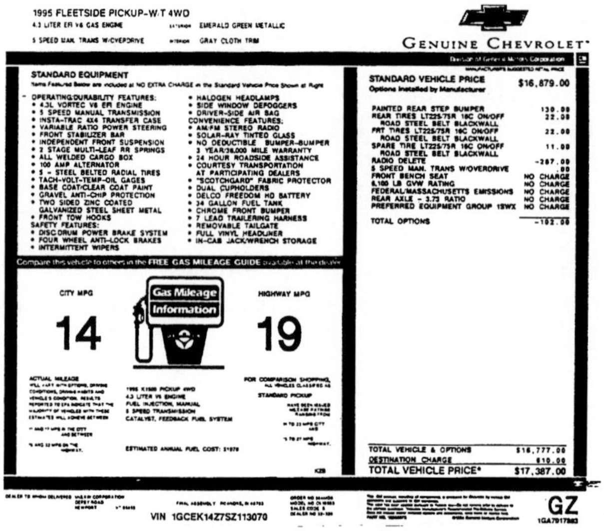

The label states that actual mileage will vary with options, driving conditions, driving habits, and the vehicle's condition. Results reported to the U.S. Environmental Protection Agency (EPA) indicate that the majority of vehicles with these estimates will achieve between 11 and 17 mpg in the city and between 16 and 22 mpg on the highway. For example, it is well known that fuel efficiency drops by 15% when changing from 55 mph to 65 mph on the highway. A heavily loaded vehicle will lose efficiency, as will a car with poorly inflated or poorly balanced tires. Driving habits and the octane rating of the gasoline used are also very important in determining efficiency.

Nevertheless, we can use these numbers to make comparisons of autos, even if we cannot accurately evaluate any one particular vehicle. It can often be very difficult to obtain all of the data needed to evaluate a car, but we can compare one car with another if we apply the same criteria to both. This is a very important function of mathematical analysis.

The label for this pickup states that the estimated annual cost of fuel is $1,078. How was this number obtained? The EPA informs us that the cost of gas is based on an average of 15,000 miles of driving each year and costs of $1.20 per gallon for regular unleaded gasoline (1995).

(continued)

8. MPG, the EPA, and the Cost of Driving *(continued)*

1. If all of your driving were on the highway, how many gallons of gasoline would you use?

2. What would this amount of regular gasoline cost?

3. Similarly, find the cost of your fuel if all of your driving were in the city.

4. What would your fuel cost if half of your driving were in the city and half on the highway?

5. The EPA estimated an annual fuel cost for this car of $1,078. How does their estimate compare with your estimate based on half city and half highway driving? Explain any difference.

6. What effect would an increase in the cost of gasoline have on the EPA estimate? on your estimate? on the difference between these estimates?

7. What estimate for mpg would you get if you assume that the city and highway mpg figures can be averaged?

8. Using the average mpg figure, find the estimated yearly cost of fuel for this pickup.

❏ Our task here is to be able to *compare* vehicles. The EPA publishes an Annual Fuel Costs Chart along with estimated mpg figures for all of the vehicles that are put on the market each year. Figure 2-2 is the costs chart for 1995.

(continued)

8. MPG, the EPA, and the Cost of Driving *(continued)*

Figure 2-2

Annual Fuel Costs Chart for 1995 Model Year Based on 15,000 Miles per Year						
Est MPG	*Dollars Per Gallon*					
	1.90	1.70	1.50	1.30	1.10	1.05
50	570	510	450	390	330	315
49	582	520	459	398	337	321
48	594	531	469	406	344	328
47	606	543	479	415	351	335
46	620	554	489	424	359	342
45	633	567	500	433	367	350
44	648	580	511	443	375	358
43	663	593	523	453	384	366
42	679	607	536	464	393	375
41	695	622	549	476	402	384
40	713	638	563	488	413	394
39	731	654	577	500	423	404
38	750	671	592	513	434	414
37	770	689	608	527	446	426
36	792	708	625	542	458	438
35	814	729	643	557	471	450
34	838	750	662	574	485	463
33	864	773	682	591	500	477
32	891	797	703	609	516	492
31	919	823	726	629	532	508
30	950	850	750	650	550	525
29	983	879	776	672	569	543
28	1018	911	804	696	589	563
27	1056	944	833	722	611	583
26	1096	981	865	750	635	606
25	1140	1020	900	780	660	630
24	1188	1063	938	813	688	656
23	1239	1109	978	848	717	685
22	1295	1159	1023	886	750	716
21	1357	1214	1071	929	786	750
20	1425	1275	1125	975	825	788
19	1500	1342	1184	1026	868	829
18	1583	1417	1250	1083	917	875
17	1676	1500	1324	1147	971	926
16	1781	1594	1406	1219	1031	984
15	1900	1700	1500	1300	1100	1050
14	2036	1821	1607	1393	1179	1125
13	2192	1962	1731	1500	1269	1212
12	2375	2125	1875	1625	1375	1313
11	2591	2318	2045	1773	1500	1432
10	2850	2550	2250	1950	1650	1575
9	3167	2833	2500	2167	1833	1750

(continued)

8. MPG, the EPA, and the Cost of Driving *(continued)*

9. The 1995 Hyundai Sonata, automatic lockup, 4-speed, 6-cylinder is rated at 18 mpg city and 24 mpg highway. The 1995 Lincoln-Mercury Sable, with identical specifications, is rated at 20 mpg city and 30 mpg highway. Compare the fuel costs for 15,000 miles of driving using gasoline at $1.10 per gallon. Assume 60% city driving and 40% on the highway.

❑ As we have seen, the EPA estimates of mpg are basically for purposes of comparison. If you want to find the actual mpg for your car or your family's car, you need not drain the tank, add a gallon of fuel, and drive until the car stops. Such an approach might provide the information you are looking for, but the car might stop in rush-hour traffic or on some deserted road far from a gasoline station.

You can obtain a reasonable estimate of a car's mpg rating by recording its odometer reading immediately after the tank is filled with gas. When the tank is nearly empty, refill it and record the odometer reading again as well as the number of gallons required to fill the tank. Dividing the difference between the odometer readings by the number of gallons added to the tank will give you a good estimate of your car's mpg rating.

A car's odometer reads 20206.0 when you fill its tank with gasoline. After driving for some time, you notice that the fuel gauge is less than $\frac{1}{4}$, so you stop to fill the tank at a service station. You find that the odometer now reads 20526.0, and 9.5 gallons of gasoline are required to fill the tank. Based on these data, the distance traveled per gallon of fuel is:

$$\frac{20526.0 \text{ mi} - 20206.0 \text{ mi}}{9.5 \text{ gal}} = \frac{320 \text{ mi}}{9.5 \text{ gal}} = 34 \text{ mi/gal}.$$

10. A car's odometer reads 45678.9 when you fill its tank with fuel. After a long drive to visit a friend, you stop for fuel. The odometer now reads 45968.4, and you find that 10.2 gallons of gasoline are required to fill the tank. What would you estimate your car's mpg to be based on these data?

(continued)

8. MPG, the EPA, and the Cost of Driving *(continued)*

11. At the start of a trip, a car has a full tank of gas, and its odometer reads 34894.9 miles. According to the map, the car has traveled 320.0 miles before the driver stops at a service station for fuel. It takes 12.4 gallons of gasoline to fill the tank.

    a. Using the data available, calculate the mpg for the car during this trip.

    b. According to the map, what should the car's odometer reading have been when the driver stopped for fuel?

    c. If the odometer actually read 35220.0 when the driver stopped for fuel, what was the difference between the trip's distance according to the map and according to the odometer?

    d. Based on the odometer readings, what was the mpg for the car?

12. If possible, determine the mpg for a car under different conditions.

    a. How do mpg values compare when the same car is driven in stop-and-go traffic versus long trips on the open highway?

    b. How do mpg values compare for a car driven in the summer versus the same car driven in the winter?

    c. How do mpg values compare for a car driven on flat highways versus the same car driven on roads that traverse mountains?

13. To obtain a more accurate estimate of your car's mpg performance, why should you keep a record of your car's fuel consumption over thousands of miles rather than the miles traveled for a single tankful of gasoline?

(continued)

Math You Really Need

8. MPG, the EPA, and the Cost of Driving *(continued)*

14. You find that on the average your car gets about 25 miles per gallon. Gasoline is selling for about $1.25 per gallon. In the course of a year, you drive this car about 20,000 miles. Oil and maintenance costs are about $30 every 5,000 miles, and insurance is approximately $1,800 per year.

   a. Estimate your fuel costs in dollars per 1,000 miles.

   b. Estimate your annual costs for oil and maintenance.

   c. Estimate your annual fuel costs.

   d. Estimate your annual total costs for fuel, oil, maintenance, and insurance.

   e. What additional costs involved in owning a car have been overlooked?

9. Buying a Car

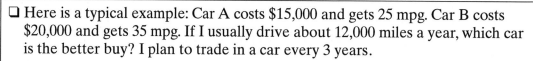

In choosing a car, you must give careful consideration to a number of factors. One important point to consider is the miles per gallon (mpg) that you can expect from a car. If you have two cars to choose from, and all factors other than cost and mpg are just about the same, which car should you choose?

❏ Here is a typical example: Car A costs $15,000 and gets 25 mpg. Car B costs $20,000 and gets 35 mpg. If I usually drive about 12,000 miles a year, which car is the better buy? I plan to trade in a car every 3 years.

One way of approaching this example is to find the total number of miles that will be driven by either car. This is clearly $12,000 \times 3 = 36,000$ miles. Since there is a difference of 10 mpg in the mileage of these cars, Car A will use:

$$36,000 \text{ miles} \times \frac{1 \text{ gallon}}{25 \text{ miles}} = 1,440 \text{ gallons.}$$

Car B will use:

$$36,000 \text{ miles} \times \frac{1 \text{ gallon}}{35 \text{ miles}} = 1,029 \text{ gallons.}$$

At an estimated average cost of $1.10 per gallon, this amounts to:

$$1,440 \text{ gallons} - 1,029 \text{ gallons} = 411 \text{ gallons}$$

$$411 \text{ gallons} \times \frac{\$1.10}{\text{gallon}} = \$452 \text{ saved by buying Car B.}$$

Since the more expensive car (B) costs $5,000 more than the cheaper car (A), it would seem that the cheaper car is the better deal. But we have not considered the environmental impact of the two cars. Nor have we considered the trade-in values.

---

1. Now you are ready to enter the car market on your own. Go to a local car dealer and explain your project. See if you can find two cars that are almost of equal value in all respects except that they have different mpg ratings and different prices. Make estimates of the number of miles that you might be driving each year and the number of years you would like to hold onto the car. Then find which car is the better buy. Be sure to write out all of the information that you have accumulated in your visit to the car dealer. Show all of your calculations.

10. Avoiding Rear-End and Multiple-Car Collisions

One car following another too closely causes the most common accidents on the highway—rear-end collisions and multiple-car pile-ups. When several cars in a line of traffic are following too closely, a multiple-car pileup may result if the lead car stops suddenly because it collides with another vehicle or an object at rest. To avoid such accidents, you must maintain a safe distance between your car and the car in front of you. But what is a safe distance? You can use mathematics and the results of carefully performed experiments to answer this question.

When a car in front of you suddenly stops, you must apply your brakes to avoid a rear-end collision. The total distance it takes your car to come to rest depends on your reaction time (the time it takes you to apply the brakes) and the braking distance (the distance your car travels after the brakes are applied). The total distance your car travels is equal to the sum of the reaction-time distance and the braking distance:

$$\text{Total distance} = \text{reaction-time distance} + \text{braking distance}.$$

Careful studies have shown that a driver's reaction time is about 0.75 second. That is, between the time a driver sees the brake light on a car being followed and applies the brakes to his or her own car, approximately $\frac{3}{4}$ of a second elapses. (The exact reaction time depends on a person's age, physical fitness, and sobriety, but we will assume a reaction time of 0.75 second in the problems that follow.)

❑ If a car has a speed of 40 mph, how far will it travel before the driver can apply the brakes; that is, what is the car's reaction-time distance?

We could find the distance in miles by multiplying the speed by the reaction time in hours. However, you can see that the time in hours and the distance in miles are small fractions.

$$0.75 \text{ s} \times \frac{1 \text{ hr}}{3,600 \text{ s}} = 0.00021 \text{ hr, and}$$

$$40 \frac{\text{mi}}{\text{hr}} \times 0.00021 \text{ hr} = 0.0083 \text{ mi.}$$

Such small fractions are not very easy to use. It is probably more convenient to convert the speed to feet per second and then multiply by the time:

$$40 \text{ mph} = 40 \frac{\text{mi}}{\text{hr}} \times \frac{1 \text{ hr}}{3,600 \text{ s}} \times \frac{5,280 \text{ ft}}{1 \text{ mi}} = 59 \text{ ft/s.}$$

In 0.75 s, the car will travel:

$$59 \text{ ft/s} \times 0.75 \text{ s} = 44 \text{ ft.}$$

Thus, the reaction-time distance for a car traveling 40 mph is 44 feet.

(continued)

10. Avoiding Rear-End and Multiple-Car Collisions *(continued)*

If you were doing a lot of problems related to traffic on the highways, the conversion factor needed to change miles per hour to feet per second would be very useful.

1. Find the conversion factor needed to change miles per hour (mph) to feet per second (ft/s).

2. Construct a table to show the reaction-time distance, in feet, for cars traveling at speeds of 0, 20, 40, 60, and 80 mph.

❏ The braking distance of a car is the distance that the car travels *after* it has traveled the reaction-time distance. It depends mainly upon the velocity of the car. It doesn't just double when the velocity doubles—it quadruples! Thus, when you hit the brakes at 60 mph, your car will travel about four times farther than if you brake at a speed of 30 mph. Of course, the wetness of the road and the condition of the tires and brakes affect the braking distance, but we will assume that the road is dry and that the tires and brakes are in good working order.

Here are some average braking distances given by the Greater Cleveland Safety Council.

Velocity (mph)	Braking Distance (feet)*
20	20 ± 2
40	72 ± 8
60	182 ± 20
80	376 ± 42

---

* The ± means plus or minus and is used to indicate the range of the results found in the experiment. For example, at 20 mph, the braking distance ranged from 18 to 22 feet.

(continued)

10. Avoiding Rear-End and
Multiple-Car Collisions *(continued)*

3. Complete the data table below for a car moving at speeds of 0, 20, 40, 60, and 80 mph.

Velocity (mph)	Reaction-Time Distance (ft)	Braking Distance (ft)	Total Distance (ft)
0			
20			
40			
60			
80			

4. Using the data in your table, plot a graph of total distance traveled versus a car's initial speed. Sketch that graph below.

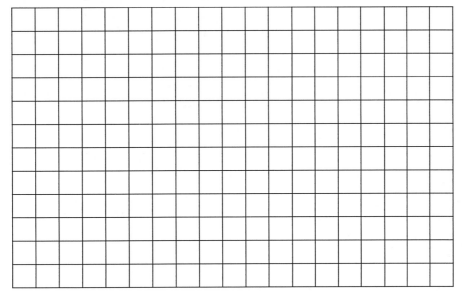

❑ Two rules are often cited in a driver's education manual for the distance that should be maintained when following another car on the open highway.
(1) The two-second rule states that the minimum time allowed for your car to travel to the position that the car ahead of you now occupies should be two seconds.
(2) The second rule generally cited might be called the car-length rule. It states that the distance between vehicles should be one car length (about 20 feet) for every 10 mph of speed. Thus, at 50 mph there should be 5 car lengths (100 feet) between cars.

(continued)

10. Avoiding Rear-End and
Multiple-Car Collisions *(continued)*

5. Use the graph that you have constructed to test the reliability of these two rules. That is, if you apply the two common rules found in driver's ed manuals, will you be able to avoid rear-end collisions when the car ahead of you:

    a. brakes to a stop without colliding with anything in front of it?

    b. stops suddenly because it collides with another vehicle or heavy object that is already at rest?

6. You may have noticed the small reflectors that line the side of many highways. You can use the spacing of these reflectors to estimate the distance that you are traveling behind the car in front of you. While driving along U.S. 91 in Vermont, a driver counted 20 spaces marked by reflectors between mile posts. This pattern was consistent except when approaching exits or bridges. What was the average spacing, in feet, between reflectors?

7. The legal speed limit on most sections of U.S. 91 is 65 mph. What is the recommended rule for following a car at this speed?

8. How can you use the reflector spacings to help you maintain the car-length spacing rule at 65 mph?

11. What Time Is It?

What time is it now in Denver? in Tokyo? in Rome? in Singapore? We often need to know the time in a distant place when making a tele-phone call. We don't want to call someone mistakenly when it's 3 A.M. their local time.

International travelers frequently consult the time zone maps that are found in the back of on-board flight magazines published by the airlines. These helpful appendices to the main body of the magazine also include valuable information on the gate plans of the various airports used by the airline. They include in-flight entertainment schedules and duty-free information as well.

Figure 2-3 is a map of the world showing time zones. The basic idea of the map is that the world is divided into 24 time zones crossing through the equator. The number below each zone tells us the number of hours that the zone differs from Greenwich Mean Time (GMT). Greenwich is near London, England; so if you live in Chicago, you'll have to do some figuring to find the time in Tokyo.

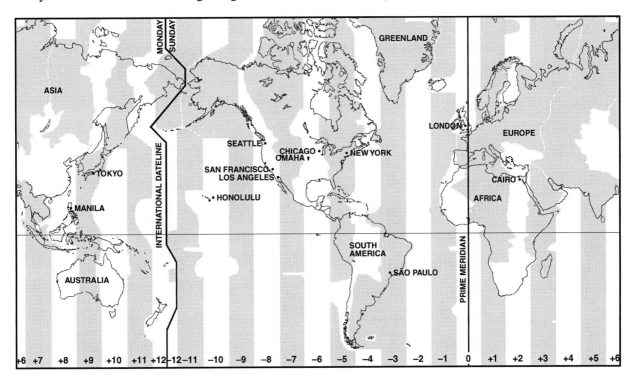

Figure 2-3

(continued)

11. What Time Is It? *(continued)*

Notice that if you move 12 hours to either the east or the west of Greenwich, you come to the International Date Line (IDL), where the date changes by one day. Because the earth turns from west to east (i.e., the sun appears to rise in the east), you must always check to see what day it is, as well as the time according to the clock.

When you fly from the West Coast to Japan, you cross the IDL and must advance your calendar one day. For example, you might leave Los Angeles at noon on Monday. If the flight takes 11 hours, you will arrive in Tokyo at 11 P.M., Monday, Los Angeles time. Tokyo is seven time zones west of Los Angeles. When you land, the airport clock in Tokyo will read 4 P.M., but since you crossed the IDL going west, it is now Tuesday. Returning to Los Angeles, you might leave Tokyo at 5 A.M., Wednesday. Eleven hours later you'll arrive in Los Angeles. It will be 4 P.M. Wednesday in Tokyo. But in Los Angeles, it will be 11 P.M. and the day will be *Tuesday*, since you crossed the IDL going east.

Figure 2-4 shows you a typical situation for the world's times. It is 4 P.M. on Sunday in New York. Moving to the west, we cross the IDL, changing the day to Monday, and find that it is 6 A.M. on Monday in Tokyo. If you imagine moving east from Tokyo across the IDL, you subtract one day and find that it is 4 P.M. on Sunday in New York. Notice that anytime you cross the date line going west, you must advance the calendar one day. Going east, you subtract a day.

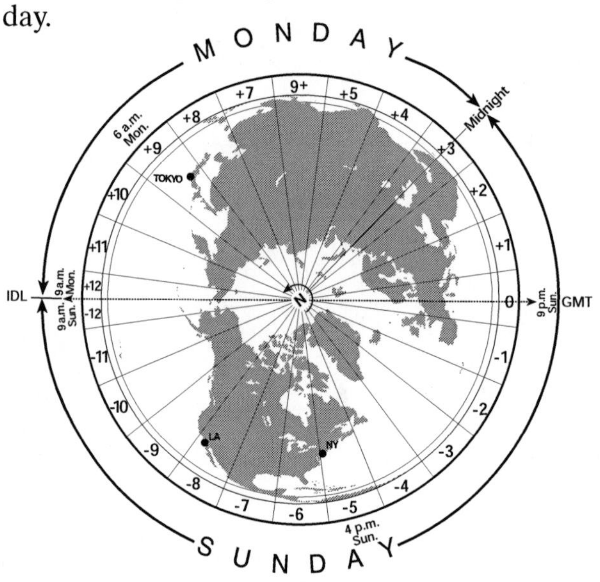

Figure 2-4

But, be careful! Figure 2-5 shows you that you must consider what happens at midnight as well as what happens at the date line. If you are going west from New York on Sunday and your watch reads almost 2 A.M. as you cross the IDL, it becomes Monday. However, two hours farther west it is almost midnight and the day is Sunday. (Remember which way the world turns!) In Tokyo, it is almost 11 P.M. on Sunday. It is also Sunday in London and New York.

(continued)

11. What Time Is It? *(continued)*

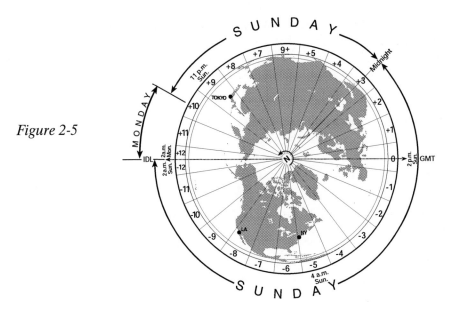

Figure 2-5

What day is it around the world when it is noon on Sunday in London? The answer: It is Sunday all around the world, but just for the instant of noon at GMT. See Figure 2-6.

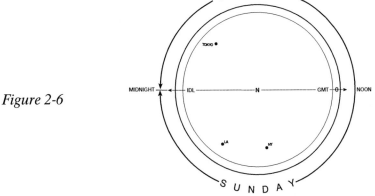

Figure 2-6

1. What is the average width in degrees at the equator of each time zone?

2. At the equator, what is the average width, in miles, of each time zone?

3. What is the average width of each time zone across the United States?

4. Why do the real time zones vary in width?

(continued)

11. What Time Is It? *(continued)*

5. If it is Sunday, late evening, in Honolulu, what time is it just west of the International Date Line?

❑ Notice that we are only able to discuss standard times using the map. Daylight Savings Time (DST) factors are not listed here. In many parts of the world, clocks are advanced one hour in the spring and set back one hour in the fall. The period between these dates is the DST period. Where and when these changes take place depends upon the individual community.

6. A few days before changing to DST, the sun rises at 5 A.M. in Boston. At about what time does the sun appear to rise a few days after Boston changes to DST?

7. What happens to the apparent time of sunset in Boston when the city changes to DST?

8. When Boston returns to standard time in the fall, what happens to the apparent time of sunrise? sunset?

9. Complete the table of equivalent times (all are standard times except where noted).

Place	Time	Place	Equivalent Time
London	5 P.M.	New York	noon
New York	5 P.M.	London	10 P.M.
London	noon Mon	Honolulu	
London	noon Mon	Tokyo	
New York	4 P.M. Sun	Tokyo	
Tokyo	3 P.M. Mon	São Paulo, Brazil	
Chicago	9 A.M.	San Francisco	
Honolulu	9 A.M.	Chicago	
New York	noon (DST)	Seattle (DST)	
New York	noon (DST)	Omaha (STD)	
Manila	1 P.M. (DST) Mon	Cairo (STD)	

12. Temperature Scales

In 1724, Gabriel Fahrenheit, a Dutch scientist, invented the mercury thermometer that we use today. In order to calibrate the unmarked scale, he chose his lowest temperature to be the position of the mercury when the bulb was immersed in an equal mixture of ammonium chloride and ice. This was the lowest temperature Fahrenheit was able to achieve, and so he called it 0°. For an upper point on his scale he chose his body temperature to be 100°.

These choices meant that all other temperatures would depend upon the two assigned fixed points and the arbitrary division of the space between them, which Fahrenheit divided into 100 Fahrenheit (F) degrees. When this thermometer was placed in boiling water, it rose to 212°F. Some years later, the two fixed points for the Fahrenheit thermometer were redefined as 32°F for the freezing point of pure water and 212°F for the boiling point of water, both measured at normal atmospheric pressure. There are 180 Fahrenheit degrees between these new fixed points. Perhaps Fahrenheit realized, in later years, that the human body temperature varies with time of day, state of health, sex, age, and method of measurement. This may have led him to redefine the fixed points using the highly reproducible freezing and boiling points of water.

In 1742, Anders Celsius, a Swedish scientist, defined the melting point of water as 0° and the boiling point of water as 100°. Since the space between these points was divided into 100 separate degrees, the scale was known as *centi*grade (°C), although it is called the Celsius scale today.

Although the Celsius scale is universally used in science and technology, the Fahrenheit scale has enough popular use in the United States that it is really useful to be able to convert from one scale to the other. Figure 2-7 shows the two scales with their fixed points aligned.

Figure 2-7

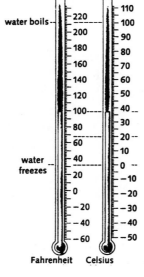

(continued)

Math You Really Need

12. Temperature Scales *(continued)*

Often both temperatures are noted when giving a weather report. However, if you must do your own conversion, then you only need to remember the basic principle that defines these scales:

	°C	°F
Boiling point, water	100	212
Freezing point, water	0	32

1. There are 180 degrees F for every 100 degrees C. How many degrees F in each degree C?

2. Suppose you are in Italy and the TV newscaster says that the temperature in Rome that day is 30°C. This means that the temperature is 30 Celsius degrees above the freezing point. How many *Fahrenheit* degrees is this above the freezing point?

3. Since water freezes at 32°F, what is the Fahrenheit temperature in Rome?

4. Now let's look at this problem the other way around. How can we go from °C to °F? There are 100 degrees C for every 180 degrees F. How many degrees C for each degree F?

5. Your Fahrenheit medical thermometer tells you that you have a fever of 103.5°F. To find the temperature in °C that you should report to a Roman doctor whom you are calling to ask for help, first find how many *Celsius* degrees this is above the freezing point. (Here you must be sure to subtract 32 degrees from the fever temperature to obtain the Fahrenheit degrees *above* freezing.)

6. Since water freezes at 0°C, what is your fever temperature in degrees Celsius?

(continued)

12. Temperature Scales *(continued)*

7. The steps that you followed in each of the above conversions can be written as algebraic expressions if you simply substitute $x°F$ and $y°C$ for the specific temperatures in the examples. Choosing the first example, write down the steps outlined above and solve for $x°F$ as a function of $y°C$. From that expression, you can then find $y°C$ as a function of $x°F$. Your answers can be fed into a programmable calculator and used for any temperature conversions.

CHAPTER 3 Music and Art

To the Teacher

Mathematics in art and music? Yes, indeed! The same Pythagoras (circa 500 B.C.) who realized the earth was a sphere also discovered that the frequency (pitch) of a vibrating string is proportional to its length. Halving the length of a vibrating string raises its pitch by one octave. The problems in this chapter will help students to see that mathematics is used in the arts as well as in the sciences and social sciences.

13. *The Mathematics of Music* (page 58)

Once you have mastered this brief introduction to the mathematics of music, you can easily find innumerable other pieces of written music to try on your students.

The main pieces of notation that have not been presented in this activity are the key signature and the clef, since neither of these factors has to do with the arithmetic of music. If you wish to add these ideas to your lesson, since they will most likely be raised by the students, point out that there are two principal clefs, the bass and the treble. Their use depends upon the range of the instrument for which the music is written.

The key signature tells us that a note must be either raised or lowered half a tone. For example, in the following key signature, F and C must each be raised half a tone. A *sharp*, #, raises a note a halftone.

A *flat*, ♭, lowers the note a halftone. The *natural*, ♮, cancels either of these alternatives.

14. *Musical Scales* (page 62)

This is a discovery activity. Even very sophisticated musicians are probably not aware that a diatonic scale can be explained by finding the ratios of the frequencies of the notes in the scale. Musicians usually refer to a diatonic scale as one having five whole tones and two semitones in a specific order, but the mathematical relationships are seldom understood. The interesting thing about this activity is for students to discover the mathematical explanation for themselves.

Answers

1. & 2.

Table T3-1: The C Major Scale (Only one octave is included.)

Vocal Note	Scale Note	Frequency (vib/sec)	Differences	Ratios
do	C	264		
re	D	297	33	1.125
mi	E	330	33	1.111
fa	F	352	22	1.067
sol	G	396	44	1.125
la	A	440	44	1.111
ti	B	495	55	1.125
do	C	528	33	1.067

3.

Table T3-2: The D Major Scale (Only one octave is included.)

Vocal Note	Scale Note	Frequency (vib/sec)	Differences	Ratios
do	D	297		
re	E	334	37	1.125
mi	F#	371	37	1.111
fa	G	396	35	1.067
sol	A	445	49	1.124
la	B	495	50	1.112
ti	C#	557	62	1.125
do	D	594	37	1.067

4. Although there is clearly no pattern to the differences in tones, the ratios of the tones, when the two scales are compared, are the same. This is the key to the formation of the Western diatonic scale.

   To understand why F sharp (F#) is so designated, notice that there is a frequency difference of (396 − 352) vib/sec = 44 vib/sec between F and G.

Adding half this difference, 22 vib/sec to the frequency of F gives (352 + 22) vib/sec = 374 vib/sec. This is just about the frequency designated for F#. We say that F has been raised a half-interval, or halftone, to F#. We can also say for that frequency that G has been lowered a half-interval to G-flat (G♭). Similarly, C# or D♭ lies about halfway between C and D.

This is not the whole story by any means. A scale that includes all the sharps and flats is called a chromatic scale. The equal-tempered chromatic scale is shown in Table T3-3.

Table T3-3: Equal-Tempered Chromatic Scale (Only one octave is included.)

Scale Note	Frequency (vib/sec)
C	262
C#, D♭	277
D	294
D#, F♭	311
E	330
F	349
F#, G♭	370
G	392
G#, A♭	415
A	440
A#, B♭	466
B	494
C	524

If you choose to bring up the chromatic scale with your students, you can ask them to do the following activity:

1. Repeat the same analysis for frequency differences and ratios that you followed for the diatonic scales.

2. What determines the frequency intervals of the twelve tones of this chromatic scale?

3. Why are there no E# or B# notes in the chromatic scale?

15. Math in Art *(page 65)*

Here is the use of mathematics where the student least expects to find it. Of course, not all of art is mathematical, but a lot of art is. Leonardo da Vinci's sketches clearly show his mastery of geometry. M.C. Escher's intriguing staircases, which so cleverly distort perspective, are fine examples of the mastery of mathematics. Encourage your students to bring to class examples of math in art that they find on their own.

Answers

1. Figure T 3-1 shows the four pieces of framing and their dimensions. Be sure that the angle is clearly labeled.

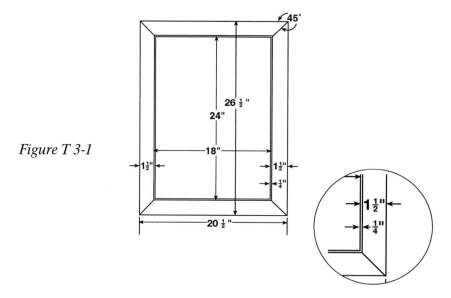

Figure T 3-1

2. The canvas has dimensions that are in the ratio 40/24, or 5/3. The dimensions of the sketch pad have a ratio of 20/16, or 5/4. The two surfaces are not similar in shape, so the sketch pad cannot be used as is.

3. If a 20-inch × 12-inch area of the pad is used, the ratio of these sides will be 20/12, or 5/3, which is the same as the ratio of the sides of the canvas.

4. If we divide the 20" side in two, we will have a 10" length. To find the width, w, that will give sketches similar in shape to the canvas, the sides of the sketch must have the same ratio as the sides of the canvas:

$$10/w = 5/3.$$

Solving for w gives a width of 6", resulting in four 10-inch × 6-inch sketches. If we had decided to divide the 16" side in two, we would have an 8" side. This would have to be the length; therefore the width, w, must be given by:

$$8/w = 5/3.$$

Solving for w gives a 4.8" width and four 8" × 4.8" sketches.

If the 8" side were to be the width, then the length, l, will have to be given by:

$$l/8 = 5/3.$$

Solving for l gives a length of 13.3". We will not be able to fit more than two sketches on a sheet.

5. Here the illusion of a three-dimensional cube is created by making all of the sides equal, although this is not true perspective.

   There are only two sizes of angles. The larger angle can be found by noting that there are three such angles at the central point. Since they fill 360°, each angle must be 120°. The smaller angle, x, can be found by noting that the sum of the four angles of each rhombus is given by:

   $$x + x + 120° + 120° = 360°;$$

   $$x = 60°.$$

6. Each edge must have $\frac{1}{4}$ inch added to it. This will make it necessary to cut five pieces of fabric, each $4\frac{1}{2}$ " × $4\frac{1}{2}$ ".

7. Figure T 3-2a shows the larger triangle. First you must draw the two 4" legs at a right angle to each other. Now connect the end points of the legs to form the hypotenuse. Draw each of the $\frac{1}{4}$ " edges on the legs. Draw the $\frac{1}{4}$ " edge on the hypotenuse so that it intersects the edges on the legs.

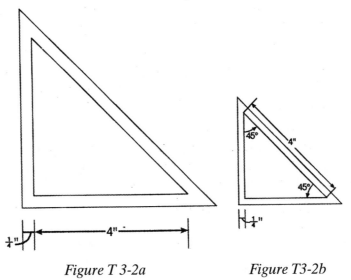

Figure T 3-2a   *Figure T3-2b*

8. For the smaller triangle, the hypotenuse is 4". Draw a 4" line on the fabric (Figure T 3-2b). Now construct 45° angles at the end points of the line. Extend these legs until they intersect to form the right angle of the triangle. Then add $\frac{1}{4}$ " seams to all of the sides.

13. The Mathematics of Music

The German philosopher Gottfried Leibniz
defined music as "an unconscious arithmetical activity of the mind in which the mind counts unaware that it is counting."

Music is usually passed from person to person by a system of writing that we call musical notation. If you look at any piece of written music, you need to know the basic mathematical ideas that are expressed. Here is a typical line from a piece of music. What does it all mean?

Figure 3-1

We begin with the five horizontal lines, called the staff:

Figure 3-2

The staff gives us a way of locating each individual note, or pitch. If the staff is preceded by a treble clef, 𝄞, then the second space from the bottom of the staff is middle A, a pitch of 440 vibrations each second. Notes are placed on alternating lines and spaces of the staff. The notes are labeled A, B, C, D, E, F, and G, and then the same letters are repeated for pitches lower or higher than the notes around middle A.

The vertical lines divide the staff into measures. All measures for a particular piece of music have the same time duration unless there is a message to indicate that the measure is to be shortened or extended in time. The actual time allotted to a measure depends on the directions of the composer or the desire of the musician.

Each musical tone is indicated by a symbol, and each symbol tells us the *relative* duration of the tone when compared with another tone in the same measure. Here are the symbolic notes and their names. The names tell us the relative duration of the note when compared with the whole note.

Whole note	Half note	Quarter note	Eighth note	Sixteenth note
o	𝅗𝅥	𝅘𝅥	𝅘𝅥𝅮	𝅘𝅥𝅯

Figure 3-3

(continued)

13. The Mathematics of Music *(continued)*

A half note is given half the time allocated to a whole note. A sixteenth note is given a sixteenth of the time allocated to a whole note.

Groups of shorter-valued notes are generally joined, as in the following examples:

 4 eighth notes   3 sixteenth notes   5 thirty-second notes

Figure 3-4

Just as there are symbols for sound, there are also symbols for silence, called rests.

Whole rest   Half rest   Quarter rest   Eighth rest   Sixteenth rest

Figure 3-5

Notes or rests can be prolonged for half their original time value by the addition of a dot.

Figure 3-6

The curved line, a *tie*, joining successive tones of the same pitch unites them into a single tone.

Following the clef symbol is the time signature. This signature is written to look like a fraction. Actually, the upper number tells us the number of beats in each measure, and the lower number, the name of the note that gets a full beat. For example, in the line shown in Figure 3-7:

Figure 3-7

the 3 tells us that there are three beats to a measure, and the 4 tells us that a fourth note (i.e., a quarter note) gets a whole beat. (If there is no notation for the time, then it is assumed that there are 4 beats to a measure and that a quarter note gets one beat. This is the same as $\frac{4}{4} = 1$.)

Figure 3-8 shows five melodies without meter signatures. See if you can add the correct meter signature to each piece. There may be more than one signature possible for a single melody.

(continued)

13. The Mathematics of Music *(continued)*

Figure 3-8

Now see if you can tap out the rhythm of the following line.

Figure 3-9

Here is a line that has changes in tone as well as a rhythm pattern. Do you recognize this line?

Figure 3-10

See if you can tap out the following lines that do not include varying tones.

Figure 3-11

(continued)

13. The Mathematics of Music *(continued)*

Here are some lines of music with complete notation. See if you can recognize them and sing them as they are written.

Figure 3-12

14. Musical Scales

Whenever a string of a guitar, or a piano, or any other musical instrument vibrates at 440 times each second, we say that the instrument is sounding the tone, or pitch, of a note called middle A.

What happens if we strike a key on the piano that vibrates at 880 vibrations/sec? This note, when sounded with the 440 vib/sec string, gives a pleasing sensation. The notes are harmonious. Likewise, 220 vib/sec, when sounded with 440 vib/sec, is harmonious. It is customary to call 440 vib/sec middle A; 880 vib/sec, A above middle A; and 220 vib/sec, A below middle A. You can play harmonious notes on a stringed instrument by simply playing the whole string followed by playing the same string at half its length.

The frequency interval between middle A (440 vib/sec) and A above middle A (880 vib/sec) can be divided in many ways. We could, for example, choose to divide this interval into five equally spaced smaller intervals. Each tone, or note, would then vibrate at a fixed frequency. We call such a set of notes a scale.

How would two notes on this scale, played together, sound? As we mentioned before, middle A when sounded with A above middle A would be harmonious. But it is not likely that most people would find pleasant harmony in any of the other combinations of notes. For this reason, no scale in which the 440 vib/sec between middle A and A above middle A is divided into five equal intervals is used by musicians.

What then makes a scale harmonious? In Western civilization, the simplest scale consists of eight familiar notes commonly called "do-re-mi-fa-sol-la-ti-do." Each note is labeled by a letter from A to G (and A again and so on) and corresponds to a particular frequency or pitch. The higher do has twice the pitch (frequency) of the lower do. But a scale can begin with do at any of the notes between A and G. For example, if we choose middle C, which has a frequency of 264 vib/sec, as do, then the middle C scale will be harmonious when divided as shown in Table 3-1. This is the C major scale, which is basic to most Western music.

Table 3-1: The C Major Scale (Only one octave is included.)

Vocal Note	Scale Note	Frequency (vib/sec)
do	C	264
re	D	297
mi	E	330
fa	F	352
sol	G	396
la	A	440
ti	B	495
do	C	528

(continued)

14. Musical Scales *(continued)*

1. Find the *differences* in frequency between each of the successive notes in the C major scale; that is, subtract the frequency for C from the frequency for D, and so on. Are there equal frequency intervals between each pair of notes of the C major scale?

2. Now find the *ratio* of each frequency to the frequency preceding it. For example, the ratio of the frequency of D to that of C is 297/264 =1.125, or exactly 9/8. What are the remaining six ratios?

❑ To find any pattern here, we will need to look at another scale. In Table 3-2 you will find the scale of D major.

Table 3-2: The D Major Scale (Only one octave is included.)

Vocal Note	Scale Note	Frequency (vib/sec)
do	D	297
re	E	334
mi	F#	371
fa	G	396
sol	A	445
la	B	495
ti	C#	557
do	D	594

(continued)

Math You Really Need

14. Musical Scales *(continued)*

3. Follow the same procedures as you did for the C major scale. That is, find the *differences* in frequency between each of the successive notes in the scale and the *ratio* of each frequency to the frequency preceding it.

4. Compare the results of the analyses of the two scales. What do you conclude?

15. Math in Art

There are many uses of mathematics in the varied fields of art. Sometimes these uses are quite obvious and sometimes not. There are so many different ways of using math in art that we can only present a few examples. You should be able to find many examples yourself by paging through art books that have reproductions and by going to museums.

1. Suppose you have an 18- × 24-inch painting that needs to be framed. Figure 3-13 shows a cross section of a piece of framing material that is $1\frac{1}{2}$ inches wide. Notice the $\frac{1}{4}$-inch inset that is necessary to press the picture against the frame. Draw a sketch of all the pieces of framing material that you will need to cut, and label all dimensions.

Figure 3-13

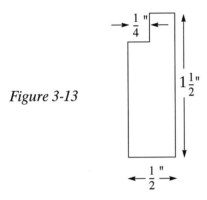

2. An artist wants to draw a sketch for a landscape that is to be on a 40-inch × 24-inch canvas. The sketch pad is 20 × 16 inches. Can the full area of the pad be used for the sketch if the finished sketch is to have a shape similar to the finished oil painting?

3. If the artist chooses to use the full 20-inch side of the pad, what should be the length of the other side of the sketch?

4. The artist wants to make four equal scaled sketches of the landscape canvas on each sheet of the sketch pad. What are the largest dimensions that each sketch can be?

(continued)

                   Math You Really Need

15. Math in Art *(continued)*

5. A quilt maker wishes to create the illusion of a cube on a flat quilt. To do this, the artist uses three diamonds. All of the sides are of equal length and are sewn together, as shown in Figure 3-14. In order to cut the material, the quilt maker must determine the size of each of the angles shown. How can you do this, and what are the measures of the angles?

Figure 3-14

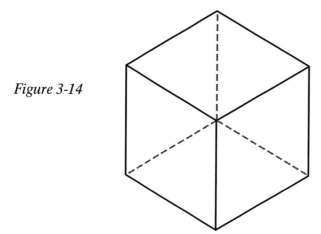

6. The mosaic pattern used by the traditional quilter is made up of five equal squares and eight triangles as shown in Figure 3-15. The triangles are of two different sizes. In order to cut the material for this quilt, the artist must include a $\frac{1}{4}$-inch seam allowance on all of the edges. This allowance makes it possible to sew the pieces together to the dimensions desired.

What must be the size of each of the pieces of material that will be used to form the squares if the finished edge is to measure 4 inches?

Figure 3-15

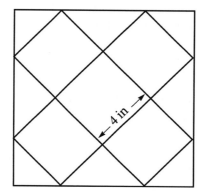

4 in

(continued)

Math You Really Need

15. Math in Art *(continued)*

7. Describe how you would go about laying out a pattern for each of the four larger triangles of this quilt.

8. Describe how you would go about laying out a pattern for each of the four smaller triangles of this quilt.

CHAPTER 4 Money

To the Teacher

It comes as no surprise that an understanding of economics, finance, and money requires mathematics. In this chapter, students will investigate just a few of the many applications of math to money.

16. Paying the Electric Bill *(page 81)*

Now is a good time to point out to the students that electrical energy is not "used up." It is changed to other forms of energy. For example, most of the electrical energy in a toaster is converted to heat; a small amount changes to light energy. In a clothes dryer, electrical energy is also converted mainly to heat, although some of it is changed to the mechanical energy that rotates the basket.

You could certainly have each student bring to class a typical electric bill. Of course, the bills from your local power company will be different in form from the bill shown in this activity. However, you can analyze your bills in much the same way as shown here. Any of the bills will allow you to calculate the kilowatt-hours per day (kwh/da) and the cost per day. Other possible calculations will depend on the information provided by your particular power company.

Answers

1. 12.5 kwh per day, as stated on the bill. This was found by dividing the 401 kwh used during the billing period by the 32 days in this period.

2. $\frac{\$40.76}{32 \text{ days}} = \$1.27$ per day

3. Yes, it does agree.

4. The VT/DPS rate of $0.05340 is $0.04227 less than the GMP rate of $0.09567. This is a difference in rate of $\frac{\$0.04227}{\$0.09567} \times 100 = 44\%$. We can also say that the VT/DPS rate is $\frac{\$0.05340}{\$0.09567} \times 100 = 56\%$ of the GMP rate. Or, the GMP rate is $\frac{\$0.09567}{\$0.05340} = 1.79$ times greater than the VT/DPS rate.

5. The average cost per kwh of $0.102 is greater than either the VT/DPS or the GMP cost per day because of the "customer charge" of $6.20 that is a part of the former figure. This customer charge is a fixed monthly charge for the use of the service facilities and does not depend on the amount of usage.

17. Budgets *(page 82)*

In keeping with NCTM standards that call for the use of mathematics as a means of solving practical problems, the questions presented here are drawn from the real world. They are very similar to those that face any librarian or library trustee in trying to resolve budgetary issues. The budget figures that appear here are very similar to those found in any small-town departmental budget.

Answers

1. $109,467 \times 1.025 = \$112,203.68$

2. $\$23,000 = 0.20 \times$ Total Budget; Total Budget $= \dfrac{\$23,000}{0.20} = \$115,000$

3. The difference between $115,000 and $112,203.68 ($2,796.32) must be taken from other parts of the budget. It is not likely that employees will agree to a cut in pay, but the staff hours might be reduced or volunteer help used to replace salaried personnel. Alternatively, it may be possible to reduce the cost of the services portion of the budget from $14,800 to about $12,000 by conserving energy, putting off all but emergency maintenance needs, and finding ways to reduce other costs.

4. Answers will vary, but it might be caused by the retirement of an older, experienced employee who was replaced by someone with less experience. A full-time employee might have been replaced by a part-time person, someone may have agreed to reduce hours of employment, or benefits to employees may have been cut.

18., 19. Business and Graphs *(page 83)*

The NCTM standards recommend that students use graphs and tables as tools to interpret expressions. Such tools, found as line, bar, and pie graphs, appear regularly in the media. It is important that students be thoroughly familiar with these graphs. To begin with, they should know how to express the meaning of the graph in words. Secondly, they should be able to interpolate and to extrapolate from a given graph.

Answers

18. *Line and Bar Graphs* (page 83)

1. It is important to label graphs meaningfully. The total expenditure for cells per year would include changing costs per cell and would not tell us the cost of the cells needed to produce a watt of power. What is wanted here is the cost of the cells necessary to produce one watt of energy.

2. The "total cost of energy per year" would not tell us how the use of solar cells has increased with time. We want to show the actual solar cell capacity for energy production that was shipped in each year.

3. a. Extrapolating the line graph to year 1998 indicates that the price of cells per watt should remain below $4 or $5. The bar graph is more difficult to extrapolate, but it indicates a range of between 75 and 85 millions of watts shipped.

   b. The year 2020 is far too great an extrapolation to make from these graphs. About all we can say is that the price of cells per watt will certainly stay below a few dollars, but the capacity shipped is impossible to predict.

   Students should probably spend some time discussing the practical problems of extrapolation and interpolation. Looking ahead, or extrapolating, a few years with these graphs is fairly reliable. Looking 25 years ahead is not. Interpolation is quite easy. We can certainly give very reliable answers for any midyear date. But ask your students about the Dow Jones average of the New York Stock Exchange. Here the picture is quite different—mostly unpredictable by either interpolation or extrapolation, especially for any individual company.

4. The data will certainly give a very smooth curve and will thus look best as a line graph for easy interpolation.

Figure T4-1

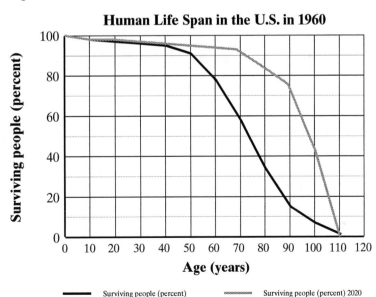

5. Since we can assume that health standards will improve over the years, the graph will shift to the right and steepen (see the dotted line in Figure T 4-1). However, the end point will still be about 115 years, the time that it takes for our human body to wear out.

6. Compared with today, by the year 2020 the United States will have a population that will include many more people in the over-65 age group. This means a larger Social Security budget, unless, of course, benefits are cut.

7. The data should be shown on a bar graph. There is obviously no regular relationship between year and deficit. However, these huge budget deficits make it more and more tempting to use Social Security funds in some way as a means of reducing the deficit. The "graying" of the population, as shown in the graph of question 5, further increases the pressure to attack Social Security.

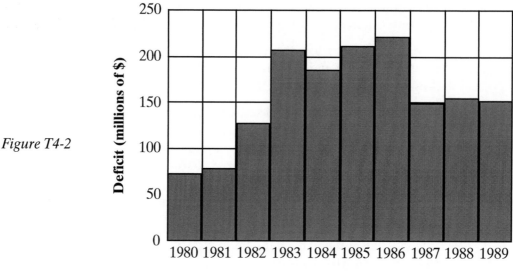

Figure T4-2

8. The student must complete the table.

U.S. Budget Deficit (billions of dollars), 1980–1989

Year	Deficit	Total Debt
1980	74	74
1981	79	153
1982	128	281
1983	207	488
1984	185	673
1985	212	885
1986	221	1,106
1987	150	1,256
1988	155	1,411
1989	152	1,563

The data is best shown as a line graph:

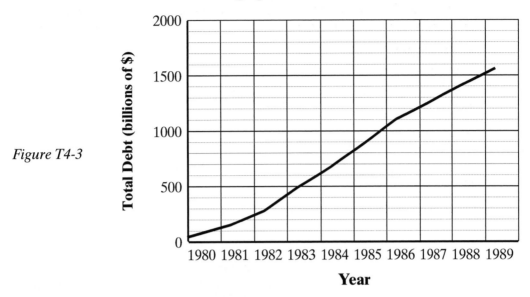

Figure T4-3

19. Pie Graphs *(page 87)*

1. First we must expand the table to show the degrees of a circle represented by each portion of the pie. For example, 43 cents is 43%, giving $0.43 \times 360° = 155°$.

The U.S. Health Care Dollar (1991)

	cents	degrees
Private health insurance	43	155
Direct patient payments	26	94
Medicare	18	65
Medicaid	5	18
Other gov't. sources (military, veterans)	2	7
Other private sources (companies, charities)	6	21

The U.S. Health Care Dollar (1991)

Figure T4-4

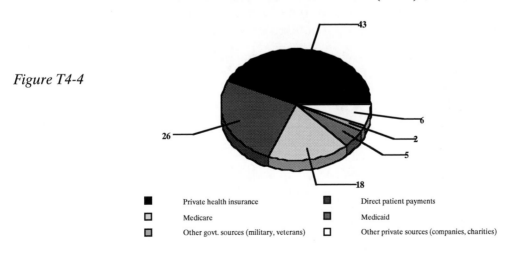

2. We have suggested that the student stick to four categories so as to simplify this problem. Of course, the percentage sum of the four categories must be 100. A typical table will look like this:

Expenditure	Dollars	% of Total	Degrees of Pie
Salaries	700,000	47	168
Maintenance	500,000	33	120
Instruction	200,000	13	48
Other	100,000	7	24

Here is the pie:

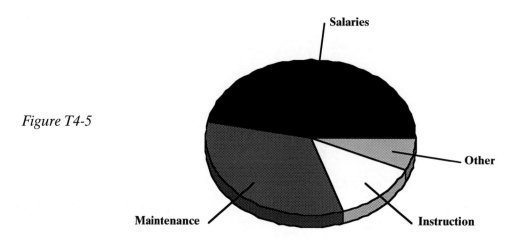

Figure T4-5

20. Paying for a College Education *(page 89)*

Paying for college involves many factors, but the cost of the standard package of tuition, room, and board is the beginning of any determination of choice. Here is a practical example of the use of raw data to construct a graph. Using interpolation and extrapolation, the graph can then be used to obtain useful information.

The graph need not be a bar graph—you could have the students make a line graph and do the same sort of analysis.

Answers

1. The bar graph below was constructed from the data table:

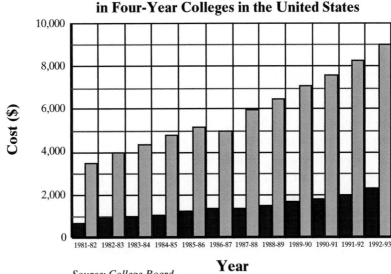

Figure T4-6

Average Annual Cost ($) of Tuition, Room and Board in Four-Year Colleges in the United States

Source: College Board

■ Public Colleges   ▨ Private Colleges

2. The student must extrapolate from the bar graphs. If, for example, your students will begin college in 1997, then a careful extrapolation of the graph predicts an average cost of $3,400 for public colleges and $12,500 for the private sector. The students can now discuss the factors that may increase or decrease these predicted costs. For example, there could be a leveling out of the increases due to a declining enrollment, consumer resistance, or less inflation of the economy. The value of the question is as much in the predicted costs as in the discussion of how one arrives at these predictions.

3. For the public colleges the average costs changed from $700 to $2,300 in the 12-year period. This is a cash increase of $1,600 and is a percentage increase in cost of:

$$\frac{\$1,600}{\$700} \times 100 = 230\%.$$

   For the private colleges:

$$\frac{\$9,000 - \$3,500}{\$3,500} \times 100 = 160\%.$$

4. By percentage, the public colleges increase costs at about 1.4 times the rate of the private colleges. But they start from a much lower base. Question 2 has helped us predict actual costs. This question and answer further serve to warn us to be wary—costs today will not likely be the costs we'll find tomorrow.

5. For the Ivy League schools:
   a. $\dfrac{\$23,250 - \$21,850}{\$21,850} \times 100 = 6.4\%.$

b. The public sector costs increased 230% over 12 years, or 19% per year. The private increase was $\frac{160\%}{12}$ = 13% per year. Your students might ask the college counselor why the costliest colleges have the smallest percentage increases.

21. Buying Land *(page 91)*

Finding the area of parcels of land is a part of everyday life for assessors, real-estate brokers, builders, and land investors as well as surveyors. It is also a useful skill for anyone contemplating the purchase of property for a home or for investment. Since measurements are usually made in feet and land is measured in acres, conversion factors are a necessary part of measuring land. The same is true in other parts of the world where land area is measured in hectares but length is measured in meters. Additional work on conversions can be found in Skill-Builder 1 on page *vii*.

Answers

1. 160 rods^2 = 160 ~~rods~~^{2} × 16.5 ft/~~rod~~ × 16.5 ft/~~rod~~ = 43,560 ft^2.

2. a. 120 yd × 50 yd = 6,000 yd^2; 6,000 ~~yd^2~~ × 9 ft^2/~~yd^2~~ = 54,000 ft^2.
   $$\frac{54,000 \, \text{ft}^2}{43,560 \, \text{ft}^2/\text{acre}} = 1.24 \text{ acres}$$

   b. $\dfrac{(90 \, \text{ft})^2}{43,560 \, \text{ft}^2/\text{acre}} = 0.19 \text{ acre}$

3. 100 m × 60 m = 6,000 m^2; $\dfrac{6,000 \, \text{m}^2}{10,000 \, \text{m}^2/\text{hectare}} = 0.60 \text{ hectare}$

4. a. 250 ft × 160 ft = 40,000 ft^2

   b. 40,000 ~~ft^2~~ × $\dfrac{1.0 \text{ acre}}{43,560 \, \text{ft}^2} = 0.92 \text{ acre}$

   c. $\dfrac{160 \text{ rods}^2}{1.0 \text{ acre}}$ × 0.92 ~~acre~~ = 147 rods^2

   d. 250 ~~ft~~ × $\dfrac{1.0 \text{ m}}{3.28 \, \text{ft}}$ × $\dfrac{160 \, \text{ft} \times 1.0 \text{ m}}{3.28 \, \text{ft}} = 3,718 \text{ m}^2$

   e. 3,718 ~~m^2~~ × $\dfrac{1.0 \text{ hectare}}{10,000 \, \text{m}^2} = 0.372 \text{ hectare}$

   f. The farmer's estimate is the best one. He was within 2 percent: $\dfrac{3}{147} = 0.02$. The real estate broker's estimate was off by 9 percent: $\dfrac{0.08}{0.92} = 0.09$; however, brokers often regard 40,000 square feet as one acre. The French colleague's estimate was the least accurate. It was off by 35 percent:

$$\frac{10{,}000 \text{ m}^2/\text{hectare}}{(0.3048 \text{ m})^2/\text{ft}^2} = 107{,}640 \text{ ft}^2/\text{hectare};$$

$$\frac{107{,}640 \text{ ft}^2/\text{hectare}}{43{,}560 \text{ ft}^2/\text{acre}} = 2.47 \text{ acre/hectare}; \quad \frac{0.92 \text{ acre} \times 1 \text{ hectare}}{2.47 \text{ acre}} = 0.37 \text{ hectare};$$

$$\text{and } \frac{0.13}{0.37} = 0.35 \text{ or } 35\%$$

5. a. Lot 1: Area of rectangle $= l \times w = 150 \text{ ft} \times 250 \text{ ft} = 37{,}500 \text{ ft}^2$, or 0.86 acre.

   Lot 2: Area of trapezoid $= \dfrac{b_1 + b_2}{2} \times h = \dfrac{100 \text{ ft} + 200 \text{ ft}}{2} \times 250 \text{ ft} =$
   $37{,}500 \text{ ft}^2$, or 0.86 acre.

   Lot 3: Area of triangle $= \frac{1}{2} b \times h = \frac{1}{2} (200 \text{ ft}) \times 250 \text{ ft} = 25{,}000 \text{ ft}^2$, or
   0.57 acre.

   Lot 4: $\dfrac{b_1 + b_2}{2} \times h = \dfrac{150 \text{ ft} + 250 \text{ ft}}{2} \times 250 \text{ ft} = 50{,}000 \text{ ft}^2$, or 1.15 acre.

   b. Lot 1: $0.86 \times \$50{,}000 = \$43{,}000$.   Lot 2: $\$43{,}000$.

   Lot 3: $0.57 \times \$50{,}000 = \$28{,}500$.   Lot 4: $1.15 \times \$50{,}000 = \$57{,}500$.

   c. $\dfrac{\$150{,}000}{3.44 \text{ acre}} = \$43{,}600/\text{acre}$

22. How Money Grows! *(page 93)*

Compound interest is a difficult concept to understand, yet it is a very important idea in all of modern financial life. In this activity the student is slowly led through the steps that result in the standard formula for compound interest. The steps require only elementary algebra and provide a very real example of the use of algebra in everyday life.

Once the concept has been developed, the student is shown how to get real answers using the y^x function on the calculator. Finally, facing reality, the student is shown how compound interest is programmed into computers in a multitude of computations. By going through the steps of this activity, the student can learn to appreciate the basic idea of compound interest and its real-life application.

Answers

1. We have found the totals for the first three years. They are:

$$T_1 = P(1 + r)$$
$$T_2 = P(1 + r)^2$$
$$T_3 = P(1 + r)^3$$

There is a pattern here, and so we surmise that:

$$T_4 = P(1 + r)^4$$

$$T_5 = P(1 + r)^5$$

$$\dotfill$$

$$T_t = P(1 + r)^t$$

2. a. After four years, with simple interest, the account will be worth the sum of the principal, $1,000, plus the four yearly $100 of simple interest:

$$\text{Total}_4 = \$1,000 + 4(\$100) = \$1,400.$$

b. Using compound interest, after four years the account will be worth:

$$T_4 = P(1 + r)^4 = 1,000(1 + 0.10)^4 = 1,000(1.1)^4 = \$1,464.10.$$

3. a. After five years, with simple interest, the account will be worth the sum of the principal, $1,000, plus the five yearly $100 of simple interest:

$$\text{Total}_5 = \$1,000 + 5(\$100) = \$1,500.$$

b. Using compound interest, after five years, the account will be worth:

$$T_5 = P(1 + r)^5 = 1,000(1 + 0.10)^5 = 1,000(1.1)^5 = \$1,610.51.$$

4. a. The y^x function on a calculator is necessary here. Using compound interest, after 20 years, the account will be worth:

$$T_{20} = P(1 + r)^{20} = 1,000(1 + 0.10)^{20} = 1,000(1.1)^{20} = \$6,727.50.$$

b. After 20 years, with simple interest, the account will be worth the sum of the principal, $1,000, plus the 20 yearly $100 in simple interest:

$$\text{Total}_{20} = \$1,000 + 20(\$100) = \$3,000.$$

5. $T_{40} = P(1 + r)^{40} = 1,000(1 + 0.05)^{40} = 1,000(1.05)^{40} = \$7,040$

6. The annual compounding of $1,000 at 10% for 20 years gave a total of $6,727. Compounding the same principal semiannually for 20 years gave a total of $7,040. The difference is due to the fact that the principal that is being compounded grows each semiannual period, earning more interest than the annual case, where the principal only grows yearly.

Banks do not absorb the difference. What they do is lower the interest rate on the semiannual account so that the yearly, semiannual, quarterly, and daily compounded accounts all produce the same totals. Working backward, what semiannual interest rate should the bank have given in our problem so that the 20-year totals would be the same? We want:

$$T_{40} = 1,000(1 + x)^{40} = \$6,727$$

where x is the interest rate. We solve for x:

$$(1 + x)^{40} = 6.727$$

$$40 \log (1 + x) = \log 6.727$$

$$\log(1 + x) = 0.02070$$

$$1 + x = 10^{0.02070}$$

$x = 0.0488$, or 4.88%, which is somewhat lower than the yearly 10% rate halved to 5%.

7. $T_{80} = 1{,}000(1 + 0.0242)^{80} = \$6{,}773$, which is very close to the total for yearly compounding at 10%. The quarterly rate is less than 10% divided by 4 and also less than 4.88% divided by 2.

8. It will be important for the student to discuss the various rates obtainable with annual, semiannual, etc. compounding. Which rate will give the highest yield? The projected yields of the student calculation and the bank calculation should agree. Ideally, the bank teller will show the student how the total is determined on a modern bank computer. From this exercise, the student should discover that one has to be very careful in choosing where to invest money.

23. Plan Ahead: Saving for Retirement *(page 97)*

This section is similar to the previous one; however, less instruction is provided here. Students are expected to make use of what they learned in "How Money Grows!" In addition to teaching students something about compound interest and exponents, this section provides a valuable lesson, albeit using simplified assumptions, about the advantages of saving at least part of one's income on a regular basis beginning at the earliest age possible.

Students who have an understanding of logarithms will find the problems easier than those who will need to use lengthier procedures.

Answers

1. $\$1{,}144.90 + 0.07(\$1{,}144.90) = \$1{,}225.04$

2. a. $1.07\,P$ or $P(1.0 + 0.07)$

   b. $P(1.07)^2$ or $P(1.07)(1.0 + 0.07)$

   c. $P(1.07)^3$ or $P(1.07)^2(1.0 + 0.07)$

   d. $P(1.07)^N$

3. By trial and error, students can find that after 10 years ($N = 10$), the value of the initial investment will be $\$1{,}000(1.07)^{10} = \$1{,}967$. If they have worked with logarithms, they may realize that since we want to know the number of years (N) for P to double, or become $2.0\,P$, at 7 percent interest, it can be represented by:

$$P(1.07)^N = 2.0\,P \text{ or } (1.07)^N = 2.0.$$

Taking the log of both sides of the equation we have:

$$N \times \log 1.07 = \log 2.0; N = \frac{0.301}{0.0294} = 10.2.$$

It will take a little more than 10 years for the investment to double.

4. $1,000(1.07)^{40} = \$14,974.46$.

5. $\$14,974.46 + \$1,000(1.07)^{39} + \$1,000(1.07)^{38} + \ldots \$1,000(1.07) \approx \$214,000$.

years	interest	years	interest
40	14974	39	13995
38	13080	37	12223
36	11424	35	10677
34	9978	33	9325
32	8715	31	8145
30	7612	29	7114
28	6649	27	6214
26	5807	25	5427
24	5072	23	4741
22	4430	21	4141
20	3870	19	3617
18	3380	17	3159
16	2952	15	2759
14	2579	13	2410
12	2252	11	2105
10	1967	9	1838
8	1718	7	1606
6	1501	5	1403
4	1311	3	1225
2	1145	1	1070

Sum $\cong$ \$214,000 (213,610 to dollar amount)

16. Paying the Electric Bill

Here is a typical electricity bill received by a customer in Vermont.

Figure 4-1

ITEMIZATION OF YOUR STATEMENT										
SERVICE PERIOD			METER READINGS		METER CONST.	KILOWATT HOURS	DEMAND	RATE	EXPLANATION	AMOUNT
FROM	TO	NUMBER OF DAYS	PRESENT	PREVIOUS						
MO DAY YR	MO DAY YR									
12 23 97	01 24 98	32	06295	5894	1	401		01	See below	40.76

Rate 01 calculation
Customer charge   6.20
VT/DPS $90 \text{ kwh} \times 0.05340 =$ 4.81
GMP $311 \text{ kwh} \times 0.09567 =$ 29.75
Total   40.76

Thank you for your payment of $34.74 made on 01/14/98
Payments received after 01/28/98 will be reflected on next month's bill

NEW BALANCE 40.76

COMPARE YOUR AVERAGE DAILY USE WITH LAST YEAR					
	DAYS	KILOWATT HOUR USAGE		DEMAND	CURRENT MONTH AVERAGE COST
		MONTHLY USE	PER DAY		PER KWH PER DAY
January 1997	34	506	14.9		
January 1998	32	401	12.5		0.102 1.27

1. How many kilowatt-hours (kwh) of electrical energy did this customer use each day of the billing period?

2. Use the New Balance figure to find the cost per day.

3. Does this answer agree with the cost per day stated on the bill?

4. VT/DPS refers to the up to 90 kwh that the state of Vermont sells to a customer each month. GMP refers to the remainder of the kwh sold to the customer by the billing company, Green Mountain Power. How do these rates differ percentage-wise?

5. Why is the average cost per kwh stated on the bill higher than either the cost per kwh for VT/DPS or GMP?

Name _____   Date _____

17. Budgets

Major budget figures for a small-town library are shown below. (To simplify matters, detailed line items are not included.) FY means fiscal year. Imagine that you are a library trustee. You and other trustees together with the librarian are negotiating with the town financial manager regarding the projected budget for the year 2002. The actual money budgeted and spent in FY 2001 is shown in the left column of figures.

	FY'01 (Actual)	Projected for FY'02
Salaries & Benefits	$77,467	$74,780
Cost of Services	$10,000	$14,800
Books, Mags, Subscr, etc.	$21,900	_____
Other	$100	$150
Total	$109,467	_____

1. The library is allowed to increase its budget by 2.5 percent. In fact, to qualify for state aid, it must increase its budget by this amount. Assuming the town would like to receive state aid, what then should be the minimum projected total budget for FY'02?

2. As a further requirement for state aid, the library's book budget, which includes magazines and other subscriptions, must be at least 20 percent of its total budget. The librarian and trustees feel they must budget at least $23,000 for books (Books, Mags, Subscr) in FY'96 to meet the needs of students, senior citizens, and other patrons. If that is to be 20 percent of the budget for FY'96, what would be the total budget figure for that year?

3. The town's financial manager refuses to allow the budget to grow by more than 2.5 percent. What might be done to resolve the matter?

4. What might have brought about the nearly $2,700 reduction in salaries shown in the projected budget figure for FY'02?

18. Business and Graphs: Line and Bar Graphs

Data presented in graphical form are commonly found in the daily newspaper and on television news programs. There are a variety of ways to graph data. Two very common ways are the line graph and the bar graph. The first three problems provide an example of an important development in the field of electrical energy production that illustrates the use of these graphs.

Photovoltaic cells are devices that are used to change light energy into electrical energy. Many of the pocket calculators that you are using today are powered by such cells grouped into solar panels. You can usually recognize a solar-cell panel by the shimmering greens, blues, and violets of the rectangular surface of the panel. Here is where solar light energy is being converted into electrical energy for your calculator.

To use solar cells to produce the electrical energy needed to run a city requires a very large investment in a very large plant. Much effort has been expended in trying to achieve this goal at a price competitive with the use of fossil fuels to provide electrical energy. The basic problem is to produce cells cheaply enough so that this goal can be reached. The following graphs show you why scientists, engineers, and businesses are optimistic about achieving such a goal in the near future.

1. The line graph below shows how the cost of solar cells has fallen in an 18-year period. Why has "cost of cells per watt capacity" been chosen for comparison over time rather than "total expenditure for photovoltaic cells per year"?

Figure 4-2

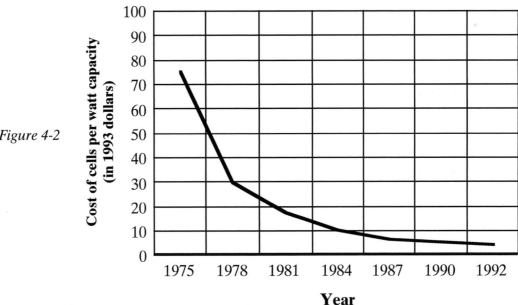

(continued)

18. Business and Graphs:
Line and Bar Graphs *(continued)*

2. The bar graph below shows how solar cell use has increased over the same years. Why has "millions of watts of capacity shipped" been chosen for the bar graph, rather than "total cost of energy per year"?

Figure 4-3

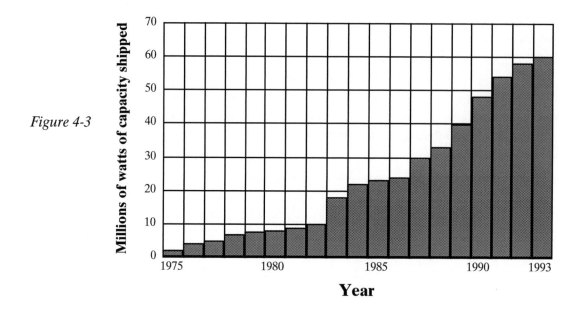

3. Using the two graphs, what can you predict for the future of this industry:

   a. in 1998?

   b. in 2020?

(continued)

Math You Really Need

18. Business and Graphs:
Line and Bar Graphs *(continued)*

❑ Social Security forms a major portion of the U. S. budget. The information that follows will help you to understand how this part of the budget will be affected by changes in human life span. Here is a table of data showing human life span in the United States in 1960.

Human Life Span in the U.S. in 1960

Age (years)	*Surviving People (percent)*
0	100
10	98
20	97
30	96
40	95
50	91
60	78
70	58
80	34
90	15
100	7
110	2

4. Decide whether these data should be shown on a line graph or a bar graph. Then graph the data.

5. On the same graph, sketch the graph that you think will represent survival in the United States as a function of age in 2020.

6. What implications do these graphs have for the Social Security budget in the year 2020?

(continued)

18. Business and Graphs:
Line and Bar Graphs *(continued)*

7. Here is a data table showing the yearly budget deficit of the United States for the 10-year period 1980–1989. What implications do these figures have for the Social Security budget in 2020?

U.S. Budget Deficit (billions of dollars), 1980–1989

Year	Deficit
1980	74
1981	79
1982	128
1983	207
1984	185
1985	212
1986	221
1987	150
1988	155
1989	152

Decide whether to display these data on a bar graph or a line graph, and then draw the graph.

8. Now use the same data to show graphically the growth of the total debt over this same period.

19. Business and Graphs: Pie Graphs

Pie graphs are used when we want to show what part of the whole—i.e., what "piece of the pie"—is represented by each of the various factors that make up the pie. Such graphs show the fractional distribution of these factors.

❑ For example, suppose you wish to show how the voting patterns in a city changed over a four-year period. Here are the data:

Voting by Party in an Eastern City (%)

	Republican	Democratic	Other
1990	35	55	10
1994	75	20	5

The Republican vote of 1990, 35%, must make up 35% of the pie. To draw an accurate pie graph, you need to use a protractor to measure degrees. Since there are 360° in a circle, the 35% Republican vote in 1990 represents 35% of 360°, or 0.35 × 360° = 126°. Here is the completed table of the voting data:

Voting by Party in an Eastern City (%)

	Republican		Democratic		Other	
1990	35	126°	55	198°	10	36°
1994	75	270°	20	72°	5	18°

Here are the two pies appropriately divided:

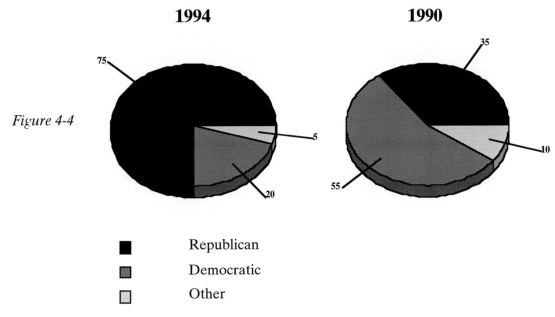

Figure 4-4

■ Republican
▨ Democratic
▢ Other

(continued)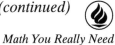

19. Business and Graphs: Pie Graphs *(continued)*

1. Here is a table of data showing how medical bills were paid in the United States for 1991. Use the data to make a pie graph.

The U.S. Health Care Dollar (1991)

	Cents
Private health insurance	43
Direct patient payments	26
Medicare	18
Medicaid	5
Other gov't. sources (military, veterans)	2
Other private sources (companies, charities)	6

2. Go to a school administrator and ask to see a copy of your school's budget. Make a table of data showing the main categories that consume the budget and their cost. For example, you might consider these main categories: salaries for teachers and administrators, building and ground maintenance, instructional costs, and "other." Now make a pie graph of these expenditures. Your table will have to include the type of expenditure, its cost, the percentage of this cost of the total expenditures, and the degrees of the pie.

20. Paying For a College Education

In making a decision as to where to go to college, there are many factors to consider. One very important factor is the cost of such an education. Basically, there are two main categories of colleges in the United States—private and public. Both include two-year and four-year colleges, but they differ considerably in cost. The prospective student must weigh the cost factor as well as other factors before making a decision.

Below is a table showing the average annual tuition, room, and board costs of private and public colleges in the United States for a 12-year period.

Average Annual Cost ($) of Tuition, Room, and Board in Four-Year Colleges in the United States*

School Year	Public Colleges	Private Colleges
1981–82	700	3,500
1982–83	950	4,000
1983–84	1,000	4,400
1984–85	1,100	4,800
1985–86	1,250	5,200
1986–87	1,350	5,500
1987–88	1,400	6,000
1988–89	1,500	6,500
1989–90	1,700	7,100
1990–91	1,800	7,600
1991–92	2,000	8,300
1992–93	2,300	9,000

Source: College Board

1. Make a bar graph of these data. The horizontal axis will indicate the years, and the vertical axis will show the cost. You can place the costs for both private and public education each year on the same bar by shading or coloring one or the other.

(continued)

20. Paying For a College Education *(continued)*

2. Use your bar graph to predict the average cost of college for *your* first year in:

   a. a public college.

   b. a private college.

3. The public colleges are much less expensive than the private colleges. However, whether or not you have tuition reduction, you'll still have to consider the annual rate of increase in cost. Find the percentage increase in cost over the 12-year period for the:

   a. public colleges.

   b. private colleges.

4. How might the answer to the above question influence your thinking in choosing a college?

5. The average costs listed above include all colleges in each category. However, the average costs for the eight Ivy League colleges are much greater. For 1991–92, the Ivy League average cost for tuition, room, and board was $21,850, and for 1992–93, it was $23,250.

   a. What was the percentage increase in tuition for the Ivy League schools in the years cited above?

   b. Compare this increase with the percentage changes in the overall public and private sectors for these same years.

21. Buying Land

One of the most common investments is land. Over the years, because of increasing population and the growing scarcity of land that has accompanied the urbanization of America, the value of property has generally grown, making it a sound investment for the speculator as well as the future home builder.

Land in rural areas is usually sold by the acre. In urban areas it is sometimes sold by the square foot. An acre was originally an area of 160 square rods. A rod, which is a unit seldom used in measurements today, is equal to 16.5 feet or 5.5 yards.

1. Today, land is usually measured in square feet and then converted to acres. What is the area of an acre in square feet?

2. How many acres are enclosed by:

   a. the lines of a football field, which is 120 yards long and 50 yards wide?

   b. the base paths of a baseball diamond, which is really a square 90 feet on a side?

3. In many parts of the world, land is measured and sold in units called hectares. A hectare is an area equal to 10,000 m². A soccer field is approximately 100 m × 60 m. What is the approximate area of a soccer field in hectares?

4. You are considering buying a rectangular building lot. The real estate agent tells you that the area of the lot is 1.0 acre. To you, the lot appears to be smaller than an acre. Your French colleague estimates it to be about 0.5 hectare. An elderly farmer who owns the adjoining land believes it to be about 150 square rods. With your tape measure, you and the farmer find that the lot is 250 feet long and 160 feet wide. According to your measurements, what is the area of the lot in:

   a. square feet?

   b. acres?

   c. square rods?

   d. square meters?

(continued)

21. Buying Land *(continued)*

e. hectares?

f. Which estimate was closest to the actual area of the parcel of land? By what percentage was each estimate in error?

5. A contractor shows you this map of building lots that are for sale.

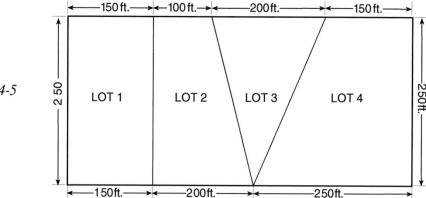

Figure 4-5

a. What is the area of each lot in square feet and in acres?

_____   _____

_____   _____

_____   _____

_____   _____

b. The contractor tells you that all the lots are for sale at the same price— $50,000 per acre. What is the price of each lot?

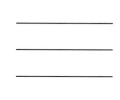

_____

_____

_____

_____

c. The contractor will agree to sell all four lots for $150,000. At this price, what is the cost in dollars per acre?

22. How Money Grows!

Investing money in a savings account is similar to planting seeds in a garden—both money and the seeds will grow if properly cared for. You'll have to water the seeds and care for the plants. The money must be attended to in a different way.

There are two ways that money can grow. The first way is called simple interest, and the second is called compound interest. Although simple interest is seldom used in real-life situations, we need to discuss it first in order to understand compound interest.

Suppose you have saved $1,000 after working at a summer job and would like to keep this money for future college expenses. If you were to put this money in a simple interest account at a bank, what would happen in the three years that will elapse before you'll want to use the money? The $1,000 is called the principal. It is the money that you start out with in your savings plan. The three years that you plan to keep the money invested is called the time of the investment. If the bank tells you that you will be earning 10% simple interest, the 10% is called the rate.

At the end of the first year, the $1,000 has earned 10% of $1,000 in simple interest. Since 10% is the same as 0.10:

$1,000 \times 0.10 = $100.

For the second year the same thing happens—the $1,000 earns $100 in simple interest. Likewise for the third year. At the end of the third year, you will have earned $300 in simple interest, and your account will be worth:

$1,000 + $1,000 \times 0.10 \times 3 = $1,300

We can write this in words as:

principal + principal × rate × time = total.

Banks do not ordinarily deal in simple interest; they provide compound interest. When you invest money in a compound interest account, the accumulated interest is continually added to the principal as the account grows. Here is how this works.

Let us find out what will happen to the same $1,000 compounded annually at 10%. At the end of the first year, the account will be worth $1,100, just as it would be with simple interest. But what will the account be worth at the end of the second year if the accumulated interest of the first year has been added to the principal and the new interest is calculated using this new principal as a base?

(continued)

22. How Money Grows! *(continued)*

To make this a bit easier to understand, let's first use some algebra. We will call the original principal P,

the compound interest rate r,

the number of years of compounding t,

and the total money in the account T.

Then, at the end of the first year, where Pr is the accumulated interest:

$$T_1 = P + Pr = P(1 + r)$$

Here, T_1 is the total money in the account after the first year.

At the end of the second year, where $P(1 + r)$ is the *new* principal and $P(1 + r)\,r$ is the interest on this new principal:

$$T_2 = P(1 + r) + P(1 + r)\,r.$$

We can factor $P(1 + r)$ from each term of this sum:

$$T_2 = P(1 + r)(1 + r)$$
$$= P(1 + r)^2.$$

Let's go through this using the actual figures.

At the end of the first year:

$$T_1 = \text{principal} + \text{principal} \times \text{rate}$$
$$T_1 = P + Pr = P(1 + r)$$
$$T_1 = \$1{,}000(1 + 0.10) = \$1{,}000(1.1) = \$1{,}100$$

At the end of the second year:

$$T_2 = \text{new principal} + \text{new principal} \times \text{rate}$$
$$T_2 = T_1 + T_1 r$$
$$T_2 = P(1 + r) + P(1 + r)\,r$$
$$T_2 = P(1 + r)^2$$
$$T_2 = \$1{,}000(1 + 0.10)^2 = \$1{,}000(1.1)^2 = \$1{,}210$$

And, at the end of year three:

$$T_3 = P(1 + r)^2 + P(1 + r)^2\,r = P(1 + r)^2(1 + r) = P(1 + r)^3$$
$$T_3 = \$1{,}000(1 + 0.10)^3 = \$1{,}331$$

(continued)

22. How Money Grows! *(continued)*

With simple interest, after three years, the account was worth $1,300. With compound interest, the total after three years is $1,331.

1. What is the formula for compound interest after four years? (Hint: Look for the pattern that gave us T_1, T_2, T_3, etc.)

    after five years?

    after t years?

2. What will the account be worth after four years with:

    a. simple interest?

    b. compound interest?

3. What will the account be worth after five years with:

    a. simple interest?

    b. compound interest?

❑ Finding the total after 20 years is difficult to do by ordinary multiplication. If your calculator has a function y^x, you can get the answer quickly. The y in y^x is the sum $(1 + r)$, and the x is the time, t. Thus:

$$y^x = (1 + r)^t$$

At the end of 20 years, the account will be worth:

$$T_{20} = P(1 + r)^{20}$$
$$= \$1,000(1.10)^{20}.$$

---

4. What is the dollar value of the account at the end of 20 years using:

    a. compound interest?

    b. simple interest?

❑ Compound interest is not always calculated on a yearly basis. Any time period is acceptable. However, if the rate is 10% yearly, then on a semiannual basis, the rate may be halved to 5%.

(continued)

95   *Math You Really Need*

22. How Money Grows! *(continued)*

5. Find the total value after 20 years of $1,000 principal compounded semiannually at 5%. (Hint: $t = 20 \times 2 = 40$.)

6. Compare the result of the annual compounding with the semiannual compounding. Explain why they differ.

7. Find the total value of $1,000 compounded quarterly for 20 years if the annual rate is 10% and the quarterly rate is 2.42%.

8. Ask at your local bank for the best interest rate that you can get if you invest $1,000 for three years. Be sure to compare yearly, semiannual, and quarterly compounding. Does your bank compound daily as well?

   What is the best rate?

   Determine the projected value of your account at the end of three years.

   Ask the bank to tell you the projected value of your account at the end of three years.

23. Plan Ahead: Saving for Retirement

You have probably heard someone say that it's never too early to prepare for the future. This is certainly true of investments that will provide income when you retire. You may find it difficult to think about retirement before you have finished your education, much less started a career, but this part of your education will enable you to see why you should begin saving for your retirement as soon as possible.

❏ Suppose you invest $1,000 at the beginning of your first working year in a retirement fund that guarantees an annual return of 7 percent. At the end of the next year, that investment will have grown to $1,000 + 0.07 × $1,000 = $1,070. A year later, your $1,000 will have a value of $1,070 + 0.07 × $1,070 = $1,144.90.

---

1. How much will your $1,000 investment be worth after three years?

2. The $1,000 is your initial principal, which you can represent by the letter *P*. How might you represent your investment after:

   a. one year?

   b. two years?

   c. three years?

   d. *N* years?

3. Approximately how long will it take before your initial investment has doubled in value?

4. Assuming you plan to retire after working 40 years, how much will your $1,000 be worth after this time?

5. If you invest $1,000 each year of your working life in this plan that guarantees an annual interest of 7 percent, how much will your investment be worth when you retire after 40 years? (Remember the money you invested at the beginning of your last year of work will earn interest for only one year. The money you invested after 21 years of work will earn interest for only 19 years, and so on.)

   Math You Really Need

CHAPTER 5   Around the House

To the Teacher

This chapter contains a number of practical problems that might confront a person around the home. All the problems can be solved using basic mathematics or simple algebra.

24. Using Math in Cooking *(page 108)*

The best way to make this lesson realistic is to have your students actually do the measurements discussed in this activity. All that is necessary are the kitchen cups and spoons shown in the illustrations. If you don't want to use real cake ingredients, you can use water or sand.

To extend the lesson, you can use any cookbook for recipes that can then be doubled or halved. Cake and bread recipes provide the most opportunities for this kind of problem in the kitchen.

You can also use eggs as an interesting problem in substitution, since different sizes of eggs obviously weigh different amounts. Most recipes call for large (2-oz) eggs. Here is a table of egg equivalents:

Hen's eggs	large	2.0 oz
	medium	1.7 oz
	small	1.4 oz

A typical problem to ask the students would be to determine the number of small eggs needed to substitute for 8 large eggs in a cake recipe. The answer is $8 \times \dfrac{2.0}{1.4} =$ 11 eggs.

Answers

1.   **Gelatin Cheesecake**

Recipe	$3 \times$ Recipe	Measurements
$\frac{1}{3}$ cup milk	1 cup milk	1 cup
A vanilla bean	3 beans	
4 egg yolks	12 yolks	
$1\frac{3}{4}$ cup sugar	$5\frac{1}{4}$ cup	5 cups + $\frac{1}{4}$ cup
$\frac{1}{4}$ tsp salt	$\frac{3}{4}$ tsp	$\frac{1}{4}$ tsp (3 times)
$3\frac{1}{2}$ Tb gelatin	$10\frac{1}{2}$ Tb	$\frac{1}{2}$ cup + 2 Tb + $1\frac{1}{2}$ tsp
$\frac{2}{3}$ cup water	2 cups	2 cups
$\frac{1}{3}$ cup lemon juice	1 cup	1 cup
$1\frac{1}{2}$ lb soft cream cheese	$4\frac{1}{2}$ lb	$4\frac{1}{2}$ lb
4 egg whites	12 whites	
$\frac{1}{2}$ cup sugar	$1\frac{1}{2}$ cup	1 cup + $\frac{1}{2}$ cup
1 cup cream	3 cups	3 cups

2. $3.5 \text{ cups} \times \dfrac{4.5}{8} = 2 \text{ cups}$

3. $\dfrac{2}{3} \times \dfrac{8}{6} = \dfrac{16}{18}$ cup, or about 1 cup (.89 cup)

4. $2 \text{ cups} \times \dfrac{6}{8} = 1\frac{1}{2} \text{ cups}$

25. Painting the House *(page 111)*

To solve the problems presented in this section, students need to make some calculations based on dimensions given in simple drawings. They will need to find the areas of rectangles and triangles, add areas, find the paint needed to cover the area, and determine the cost of doing the job. The problems provide another opportunity to stress unit analysis.

The first four problems are quite straightforward. Problem 5 involves some conversions and requires some thoughtful analysis. The student must see that the volume of paint applied to the house is spread over the entire area. Therefore, the product of the paint's thickness and the surface area over which it is spread should equal the volume of the paint applied to the house.

If it seems appropriate for the students you teach, you might like to extend the section by asking students, either individually or in small groups, to apply what they have learned to their own homes or rooms or to sections of the school (either inside or outside). In keeping with NCTM standards, it provides a real-world situation that gives students an opportunity to make approximations and value judgments, apply mathematical modeling to real-world problems, and use a great deal of common sense.

The most difficult dimension of a house to measure is the height to the peak of the roof. Rather than encourage students to climb ladders, you might introduce this activity with a class discussion of how this measurement can be found. One approach, for example, would be to measure one shingle or one clapboard and then count the number from the foundation to the peak. The real test will be when students actually apply theoretical suggestions about making measurements to a real house. You might ask them to do the following.

1. Use a long tape measure to measure the dimensions of the house or other building. Draw a scaled sketch of the house or building including all of the dimensions.

2. Show how you calculate the total surface area that needs to be painted.

3. From the instructions on a can of exterior primer, find the area covered by a gallon of the paint and calculate the number of gallons required and the total cost.

4. Do the same calculations for the finish coat. With this information, you would be ready to actually go to the paint store and buy the paint needed for the house.

In reviewing students' results:

1. Insist on a carefully drawn and dimensioned rendering of the house that is to be painted. There are lots of judgment calls in this work, and you can ask the students many questions, especially how the dimensions were actually measured. This applies most importantly to the peak of the roof.

2. Students should set out the calculations in detail so they can easily check and verify that each surface is accounted for.

3. Students should record the name, type, and price of the paint they have chosen. This involves a trip to the paint store or a review of newspaper ads so students can use a real price.

Answers

1. $1 \text{ ft} = \frac{1}{16} \text{ in}$

2. Each end of the house (north and south sides) can be thought of as a triangle with a 12-foot height and a 10-foot base and a trapezoid with 12- and 8-foot heights and a 10-foot base set on a rectangle 20 feet long and 8 feet high. The total surface area to be painted on the ends is therefore:

    area of rectangle = $20 \text{ ft} \times 8 \text{ ft} = 160 \text{ ft}^2$.

    area of triangle = $\frac{1}{2} \times 10 \text{ ft} \times 12 \text{ ft} = 60 \text{ ft}^2$.

$$\text{area of trapezoid} = \tfrac{1}{2}\,(12\text{ ft} + 8\text{ ft}) \times 10\text{ ft} = 100\text{ ft}^2.$$

$$\text{total area of ends} = 2(60\text{ ft}^2 + 160\text{ ft}^2 + 100\text{ ft}^2) = 640\text{ ft}^2.$$

The front and rear of the house can be thought of as rectangles with areas of:

$$\text{front of house} = 40\text{ ft} \times 8\text{ ft} = 320\text{ ft}^2.$$

$$\text{back of house} = 40\text{ ft} \times 16\text{ ft} = 640\text{ ft}^2.$$

$$\text{total area of front and back} = 320\text{ ft}^2 + 640\text{ ft}^2 = 960\text{ ft}^2.$$

$$\text{total area to be painted} = 640\text{ ft}^2 + 960\text{ ft}^2 = 1{,}600\text{ ft}^2.$$

3. $1{,}600\text{ ft}^2 \times \dfrac{1.0\text{ gal}}{400\text{ ft}^2} = 4.0$ gal; 4.0 gal/coat $\times$ 2 coats = 8.0 gal.

4. You buy 8.0 gallons, so $8 \times \$18/\text{gal} = \$144$.

5. $8.0\text{ gal} \times \dfrac{231\text{ in}^3}{1.0\text{ gal}} = 1{,}848\text{ in}^3$. Thickness = volume/area =

   $1{,}848\text{ in}^3/1{,}600\text{ ft}^2 \times 144\text{ in}^2/\text{ft}^2 = 0.0080\text{ in}.$

26. Degree-Days, Fuel, and Heating Costs *(page 113)*

A major expense for many homeowners and renters is the cost of heating their dwelling during the winter. The first seven problems in this section have to do with the primary cause of heating bills; that is, cold weather and the associated unit of degree-days that heating engineers and fuel companies use to determine the severity of the heating season. Problems 8 to 10 involve economic considerations centered on the cost of installing different heating systems.

Answers

1. The degree-days for the week from Sunday to Saturday were, in that order, $30 + 22 + 33 + 20 + 35 + 40 + 45 = 225$ DD for the week.

2. a. The sum of the month-by-month degree-days for the heating season is 6,107 DD.

   b. The 6,107 DD is only 20 DD less than the 6,127 DD average for a 30-year period.

3. Fairbanks

4. Honolulu

5. It would cost about twice as much to heat a home in Duluth as it would to heat a comparable home in New York—10,000 DD/4,848 DD = 2.06.

6. a. $14{,}279/4{,}792 \times \$1{,}000 = \$2{,}980$

   b. $3{,}095/4{,}792 \times \$1{,}000 = \$646$

c. $206/4{,}792 \times \$1{,}000 = \$43$

7. It was assumed that the heating system and fuel prices were the same.

8. a. $\$28/\text{M Btu} \times 50 \text{ M Btu} = \$1{,}400$

   b. $\$7/\text{M Btu} \times 50 \text{ M Btu} = \$350$; however, the oil system is only 75% efficient. Therefore, $\$350$ is only 75% of the actual heating cost. The actual cost will be: $0.75 \times ? = \$350$; $? = \$350/0.75 = \$467$.

   c. $\dfrac{\$8/\text{M Btu} \times 50 \text{ M Btu}}{0.80} = \$500$

9. a. $\$2{,}500 + \$1{,}400 = \$3{,}900$

   b. $\$6{,}000 + \$467 = \$6{,}467$

   c. $\$5{,}000 + \$500 = \$5{,}500$

10. a. Saving $= (\$6{,}000 - \$2{,}500) = \$3{,}500$. Difference in fuel costs $= \$1{,}400 - \$467 = \$933$; $\dfrac{\$3{,}500}{\$933/\text{yr}} = 3.75$ years.

    b. Saving $= \$5{,}000 - \$2{,}500 = \$2{,}500$. Difference in fuel costs $= \$1{,}400 - \$500 = \$900$; $\dfrac{\$2{,}500}{\$900/\text{yr}} = 2.78$ years.

27. The Usable Energy from Household Lightbulbs *(page 117)*

The NCTM standards emphasize that the same starting materials can be used for a group of students of varying abilities. Here is an example of an exercise that can be developed for different levels of mathematical ability.

This is an example of a very practical use of mathematics. The student collects the data and then does the analysis. But the exercise need not stop with the last question. What follows are some suggestions for extending the basic lesson well beyond the elementary level.

What about the cost of using a lightbulb? To analyze this problem, we need to do some careful application of mathematics, even though the computation itself is not difficult. You can lead your students through this task by asking questions.

The lightbulb that gives the highest percentage of usable light is the most efficient bulb. But this is not necessarily the "best buy" bulb. To find the "best buy" bulb, you need to know the amount of light energy delivered by each bulb over its lifetime. The cost of this energy is the sum of the cost of the bulb plus the cost of operating the bulb over its lifetime. Dividing the light energy by the total cost will allow us to compare the energy per dollar of various bulbs and decide on the "best buy."

The total energy, in kilowatt-hours, to operate a bulb over its lifetime is given by:

$$\text{bulb wattage} \times \frac{1}{1{,}000} \times \text{average life (in hours)}.$$

For example, a 100-W bulb with an average life of 750 hours uses:

$$100 \text{ W} \times \frac{1 \text{ kw}}{1,000 \text{ W}} \times 750 \text{ hr} = 75 \text{ kwh of energy.}$$

The same bulb, as we learned above, delivers only 2.5 W of usable light; therefore, in its lifetime it provides:

$$2.50 \text{ W} \times \frac{1 \text{ kw}}{1,000 \text{ W}} \times 750 \text{ hr} = 1.88 \text{ kwh of usable light energy.}$$

To find the cost of this energy, you need to know how much your electric company charges per kilowatt-hour. Now you can determine the total cost of the energy to operate each bulb over its average lifetime. Be sure to include the original cost of the bulb. For example, suppose the 100-W bulb with an average lifetime of 750 hours described above costs $0.75. If electricity costs $0.10 per kwh, then the total cost of operating this bulb over its average lifetime is:

$$0.100 \text{ kw} \times 750 \text{ h} \times \frac{\$0.10}{\text{kwh}} + \$0.75 = \$8.25.$$

The answer to our original question— namely, How much light energy does the bulb provide per dollar?—can be found by dividing the total usable light energy by its cost. In our example, the bulb provides 0.228 kwh of usable light energy for a dollar, because:

$$\frac{1.88 \text{ kwh}}{\$8.25} = 0.228 \text{ kwh/\$.}$$

You can now find the amount of usable light energy delivered per dollar by each of the bulbs in your data table. Which bulb is the "best buy"?

This brings up further questions, such as: "Might two bulbs or three bulbs of lower wattage be a better buy than one higher-wattage bulb?"

The "best buy" bulb provides the most usable light energy per dollar, but it may or may not be the most environmentally sound bulb to buy. We saw in the previous calculations that a 100-W bulb delivers only 2.50 W of usable energy. Since efficiency is the ratio of the useful energy output to the total energy input, this bulb is not very efficient. In fact, its efficiency is only:

$$\frac{2.50 \text{ W}}{100 \text{ W}} \times 100 = 2.5\%.$$

Answers

1. The cost of electrical energy varies throughout the country. It should be somewhere around $0.10 per kwh.

2. The table of data that will need to be filled in is as follows:

Total Wattage	Lumens	Usable Wattage	Efficiency (%)
100	1,710	2.50	2.5
	etc.		

3. The answer will appear in the table.

28. Lumber and Board Feet *(page 119)*

In this section, lumber measurements are employed to illustrate the use of mathematics in a very practical and vital industry. NCTM standards suggest that students examine real-world problems using geometry and trigonometric functions, that they construct and use tables and graphs, and that they represent relationships between variables with equations. This section provides students with opportunities to do all these things.

The use of scientific notation and significant figures would be useful here. For more information and practice problems regarding scientific notation and significant figures, see Skill-Builders 2 and 3 on pages *xii* and *xv*, respectively.

Answers

1. 12 in × 12 in × 1 in = 144 in^3

2. 144 in^3/1,728 in^3/ft^3 = 0.083 ft^3 = 1/12 ft^3

3. 2 in × 4 in × 120 in = 960 in^3; 960 in^3/144 in^3/bd ft = 6.7 bd ft; \$1.00/6.7 bd ft = \$0.15/bd ft, or 15¢/bd ft

4. Students will vary in their methods of developing a table, but the basic approach must be to determine the number of board feet in various lengths of 2 × 4's. This involves finding the total number of cubic inches in the piece of lumber and dividing by 144 in^3/bd ft.

Length (ft)	Board Feet in 2 × 4's
6	4.0
7	4.7
8	5.3
10	6.7

You might ask students to prepare such tables for other cuts of lumber such as 2 × 6's, 4 × 4's, 2 × 8's, etc.

5. The number of board feet is proportional to the length. Thus, a 2 × 4 that is 16 feet long will have twice the board feet of one that is 8 feet long.

6. a. From 5.5 feet above the ground at a point 20 feet from the tree, the angle to the tree's top is 72°. Students who have a grasp of basic trigonometric functions should see that the tangent of the angle as shown in Figure 5-4 will be the ratio of *h* (the height of the tree less 5.5 ft) to the distance from the tree, which is 20 feet. Thus:

    $$\tan 72° = h/20 \text{ ft; and } h = \tan 72° × 20 \text{ ft} = 3.1 × 20 \text{ ft} = 62 \text{ ft.}$$

    The total height of the tree is 62 ft + 5.5 ft = 67.5 ft.

Students unfamiliar with trigonometry can make scale drawings to determine the tree's height.

b. Since the tree will be cut one foot above the ground, the length of the tree's trunk after cutting will be 66.5 feet.

c. We assume the tree's trunk to be a cone. Its volume, therefore, is:

$$\tfrac{1}{3}\pi r^2 h = \tfrac{1}{3}\pi (2.0 \text{ ft})^2 \times 66.5 \text{ ft} = 2.8 \times 10^2 \text{ ft}^3.$$

d. $2.8 \times 10^2 \text{ ft}^3 \times 1{,}728 \text{ in}^3/\text{ft}^3 = 4.8 \times 10^5 \text{ in}^3$; $4.8 \times 10^5 \text{ in}^3/144 \text{ in}^3/\text{bd ft}$ $= 3.4 \times 10^3 \text{ bd ft}$

e. The diameter of the base without bark would be 4 feet less 4 inches, or 3.7 feet (to two significant figures). The volume of the solid wood then would be:

$$\tfrac{1}{3}\pi r^2 h = \tfrac{1}{3}\pi (3.7/2)^2 \times 66.5 \text{ ft} = 2.4 \times 10^2 \text{ ft}^3, \text{ or } 2.9 \times 10^3 \text{ bd ft.}$$

7. a. By drawing two diameters perpendicular to one another and connecting the ends of the diameters with straight lines, a square can be inscribed within a circle (Figure 5-5). The diagonal of the square is the diameter of the circle. From the Pythagorean theorem, we know that the square of the diameter, which is the diagonal of the square, will equal twice the length of the square.

$$d^2 = 2l^2; \; l^2 = d^2/2 = (3.0 \text{ ft})^2/2 = 4.5 \text{ ft}^2; \; l = 2.1 \text{ ft}$$

b. $4.5 \text{ ft}^2 \times 16 \text{ ft} = 72 \text{ ft}^3$; $\dfrac{72 \text{ ft}^3 \times 1{,}728 \text{ in}^3/\text{ft}^3}{144 \text{ in}^3/\text{bd ft}} = 864 \text{ bd ft.}$

8. $8 \text{ ft} \times 4 \text{ ft} \times 4 \text{ ft} = 128 \text{ ft}^3$

9. a. The length of the log will not affect the fraction of the volume, but logs with a square cross section could be stacked to fill the space within a cord. Circular logs take up only:

$\dfrac{\pi(d/2)^2}{d^2}$ of the total volume, which equals $\dfrac{\pi}{4} = 0.785$, or 78.5% of the volume.

b. $1.000 - 0.785 = 0.215$, or 21.5% would be air

c. The actual volume would probably be less. Wood logs are not identical, nor are they generally stacked with great care.

10. a. Both pieces of information confirm that the actual volume of wood in a cord is less than 0.785 of the total.

For oak: $52.0 \text{ lb/ft}^3 \times 128 \text{ ft}^3/\text{cord} = 6{,}660 \text{ lb/cord} = 3.33 \text{ tons/cord}$

2.20 tons/cord/3.33 tons/cord = 0.661, indicating that only 66% of a cord is actually wood.

For maple: $45.0 \text{ lb/ft}^3 \times 128 \text{ ft}^3/\text{cord} = 5{,}760 \text{ lb/cord} = 2.88 \text{ tons/cord.}$

2.05 tons/cord/2.88 tons/cord = 0.712, indicating that only 71% of a cord is actually wood.

b. The straight line graph (Figure T 5-1) indicates that the energy content of wood is directly proportional to the density of the wood:

Energy content (MBtu/cord) = 14.2 MBtu/ton × density (tons/cord)

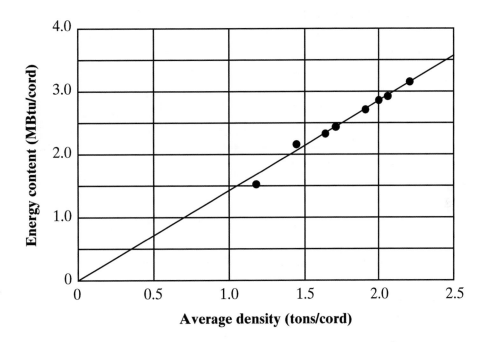

Figure T 5-1

24. Using Math in Cooking

Good cooks know that cake recipes must be exact. If exactly one tablespoon of baking powder is called for, then a tablespoon and a quarter can often wreak disaster. This would certainly not be true of a soup. It hardly matters whether we add a cup of chopped celery or two cups in most any soup.

Suppose you have your grandmother's favorite cake recipe to prepare. However, you know that you want a cake only one half as big as the huge extravaganza that Grandma prepared each Christmas. The starting point of any recipe is the set of cup measurements that are usually found in an American kitchen. They are pictured in Figure 5-1:

Figure 5-1

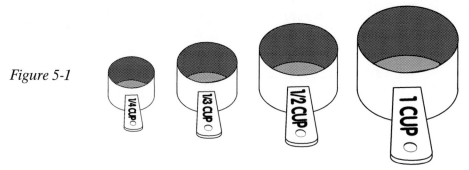

Along with the cup measurements, most kitchens have a set of tablespoon and teaspoon measurements. They are shown in Figure 5-2.

Figure 5-2

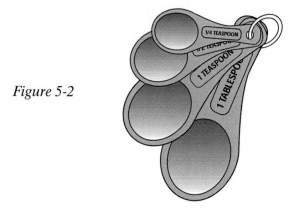

(continued)

24. Using Math in Cooking *(continued)*

❏ Now suppose that Grandma's recipe calls for $5\frac{2}{3}$ cups of cake flour. You will need just one half of this amount. Here is one way to figure this: 5 cups is 15 thirds; 15 thirds and 2 thirds is 17 thirds. You need half of this amount, or $8\frac{1}{2}$ thirds. This is not a convenient amount to take with our set of measuring cups and tablespoons if it is important to measure exactly.

A more convenient method is to take half of 5 cups and half of $\frac{2}{3}$ cup. This gives us $2\frac{1}{2}$ cups plus half of $\frac{2}{3}$ cup ($\frac{1}{3}$ cup). Each of these amounts is easy to measure with our equipment, since we need a cup measure, a half cup, and a third cup.

Suppose the same recipe calls for $\frac{3}{4}$ cup butter. You need half this quantity. What will you do? Since half of $\frac{3}{4}$ cup butter is $\frac{3}{8}$ cup, you don't have an appropriate way of measuring an exact amount of butter. The solution is found in knowing just two equivalent measures:

> 1 tablespoon = 3 teaspoons.
>
> 16 tablespoons = 1 cup.

Since there are 16 tablespoons in a cup, $\frac{3}{4}$ of 16 = 12 tablespoons. Half of this amount is 6 tablespoons, an amount you can measure easily with the tablespoon measure.

Here are the ingredients for a cake that needs to be tripled to make it suitable for a large crowd.

Gelatin Cheesecake

$\frac{1}{3}$ cup milk

A vanilla bean

4 egg yolks

$1\frac{3}{4}$ cup sugar

$\frac{1}{4}$ teaspoon salt

$3\frac{1}{2}$ tablespoons gelatin

$\frac{2}{3}$ cup water

$\frac{1}{3}$ cup lemon juice

$1\frac{1}{2}$ pounds soft cream cheese

4 egg whites

$\frac{1}{2}$ cup sugar

1 cup whipping cream

(continued)

Name _____ Date _____

24. Using Math in Cooking *(continued)*

1. Make a list of how you can most conveniently measure each of these ingredients, tripled in quantity, utilizing the measuring cups and spoons shown in Figures 5-1 and 5-2.

❏ Another problem we often encounter in cooking is the matter of substitution of ingredients. A common example is sugar. Here is a table of sugar equivalents:

1 cup granulated sugar = 8 ounces (oz)

1 cup confectioners' sugar = $4\frac{1}{2}$ oz

1 cup brown sugar = 6 oz

You're a new cook, and you run out of granulated sugar while mixing together the ingredients of a cake. You need $2\frac{1}{2}$ cups more of granulated sugar. There's plenty of confectioners' sugar around the kitchen. How much confectioners' sugar should you substitute for $2\frac{1}{2}$ cups of granulated sugar? The answer is surely around twice as much confectioners' as granulated, since a cup of granulated weighs about twice as much as a cup of confectioners', i.e., approximately $\frac{8}{4}$. To get the exact answer that we will need for cake measurement, we can say that it takes $\frac{8}{4\frac{1}{2}}$ as much confectioners'; therefore, the amount of confectioners' sugar needed is:

$$\frac{8}{4\frac{1}{2}} \times 2\frac{1}{2} \text{ cups} = 4.44 \text{ cups.}$$

You'll have to use four cup measurements plus a little less than a half-cup measure. (Or you can calculate the number of tablespoons in 0.44 cup: This gives 0.44×16 Tb = 7 Tb. So you can take 4 cups plus 7 Tb confectioners' in place of $2\frac{1}{2}$ cup granulated.)

---

2. Suppose you run out of confectioners' sugar but have plenty of granulated. How much granulated is needed to replace $3\frac{1}{2}$ cups confectioners'?

3. How much brown sugar is need to replace $\frac{2}{3}$ cup granulated, assuming that the difference in flavor would not be important?

4. How much granulated sugar is necessary to replace 2 cups brown sugar?

25. Painting the House

This question is one that confronts many homeowners. Suppose that you own a home. The roof, which is covered with asbestos shingles, is in excellent condition, but the wooden clapboards on the side of the house should be painted. You scrape away the old paint and find that you have plenty of brushes. You plan to apply a coat of primer and a finish coat. But how much paint should you buy?

❏ You make a trip to the hardware store and find that a gallon of good-quality paint will cover about 400 square feet. But how many square feet do you have to paint?

You return to your house, make some measurements, and prepare four simple drawings of the sides of your house as shown in Figure 5-3.

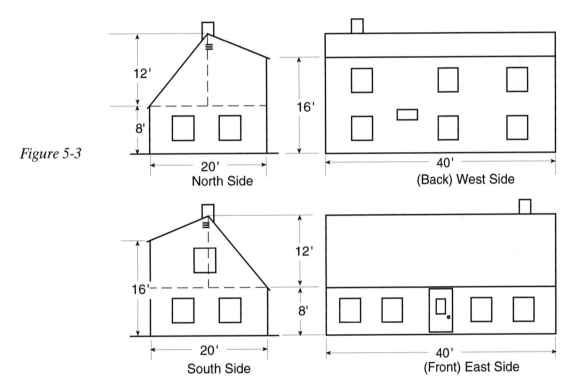

Figure 5-3

1. What scale was used to draw the sides of the house shown in the drawings?

(continued)

111   *Math You Really Need*

25. Painting the House *(continued)*

2. What is the total surface area to be painted? (You might argue that the area taken up by the windows should be subtracted from the total area. However, you may want to paint the frames of these windows, and it is always wise to plan on extra paint in case the wood in some areas is particularly dry. So don't bother to subtract the area of the windows from the total area to be painted.)

3. Remembering that you will have to apply two coats—a primer coat and a finish coat—how much paint should you buy to paint this house?

4. If the paint sells for $18 per gallon, how much will it cost to paint the house?

5. A gallon contains 231 cubic inches (in^3). Use this information to figure out how thick the paint on the house will be when you complete the job.

26. Degree-Days, Fuel, and Heating Costs

Homeowners are always concerned about heating costs. The fuel required to heat a house depends on the temperature of the air outside the building. The colder the air, the greater the heating cost, because the rate that heat flows from a house is proportional to the difference between the temperatures inside and outside the building. If the temperature difference is 20°, it will require twice as much heat to keep the building warm as it will if the temperature difference is 10°.

Heating engineers developed a unit to help homeowners anticipate their heating costs. That unit is the degree-day. As the name of the unit implies, a degree-day is the product of a temperature and a time period measured in days. The degrees in a degree-day are the difference between 65° Fahrenheit (F) and the temperature of the outside air. If, on a certain day, the average outside temperature is 45°F, the number of degree-days for that day is equal to the difference between 65°F and 45°F times one day:

$$(65°F - 45°F) \times 1 \text{ day} = 20 \text{ degree-days (DD)}.$$

If the average temperature for the following day is 35°F, the total number of degree-days for the two days is 50 DD:

$$[(65°F - 45°F) \times 1 \text{ day}] + [(65°F - 35°F) \times 1 \text{ day}] = 20 \text{ DD} + 30 \text{ DD} = 50 \text{ DD}.$$

1. During a January in Chicago, the average temperatures for a week were recorded in the table below.

Sunday	Monday	Tuesday	Wednesday	Thursday	Friday	Saturday
35°F	43°F	32°F	45°F	30°F	25°F	20°F

What was the total number of degree-days for that week?

By doing similar calculations for every day of a heating season, the total number of degree-days can be found for an entire year. As you might expect, in North America the number of degree-days tends to increase as you move northward. However, the total number of degree-days for any given location remains relatively constant from year to year. An extremely cold January is often counterbalanced by a mild February. Table 5-1 lists the number of degree-days for a number of U.S. cities.

Table 5-1: Number of Degree-Days Per Year for Various U.S. Cities
Averaged over a 30-Year Period

City	Degree-Days	City	Degree-Days
Atlanta, GA	3,095	Honolulu, HI	0
Chicago, IL	6,127	Miami, FL	206
Duluth, MN	10,000	New York, NY	4,848
Fairbanks, AK	14,279	Portland, OR	4,792

(continued)

26. Degree-Days, Fuel, and Heating Costs *(continued)*

2. The numbers of degree-days for a nine-month heating season in Chicago are shown below.

Sept.	Oct.	Nov.	Dec.	Jan.	Feb.	Mar.	Apr.	May
81	326	753	1,113	1,209	1,044	890	480	211

   a. What was the total number of degree-days for this heating season in Chicago?

   b. How did this heating season compare with the average over a 30-year period as shown in Table 5-1?

3. In which U.S. city would your heating costs be greatest?

4. In which U.S. city would your heating costs be least?

5. How would the the cost of heating a house in Duluth compare with the cost of heating an identical house in New York City?

6. It costs $1,000 per year to heat a certain house in Portland, Oregon. To the nearest dollar, how much would it cost to heat an identical house in:

   a. Fairbanks?

   b. Atlanta?

   c. Miami?

7. What assumptions did you make in answering questions 5 and 6?

   You decide to buy an unfinished house, and the heating system has not yet been installed. Based on the number of degree-days for a heating season and the insulation already in place, the heating requirements for the building are estimated to be 50,000,000 British thermal units (Btus). (A Btu is a unit of heat. It is the amount of heat required to raise the temperature of one pound of water by 1°F.)

(continued)

26. Degree-Days, Fuel, and Heating Costs *(continued)*

Following some research, you develop Table 5-2. The table shows the cost of each type of heating system in dollars per million Btus and the efficiency of each system. Electric heat is expensive, but it is very efficient—none of the heat goes up the chimney. Oil and natural gas are less expensive, but some of the potential heat stored in the fuel is lost because the fuel does not burn completely or because some of the heat goes up the chimney and is not used to heat the building. Therefore, less than 100 percent of the energy stored in the fuel is available to heat the house. Suppose a gallon of fuel oil contains 100,000 Btus of energy. If the oil furnace is only 75 percent efficient, then burning a gallon of fuel oil provides only 75,000 Btus to heat the building. The remaining 25,000 Btus are not available to heat living space.

Table 5-2: Comparative Costs of Different Heating Systems

Source of Heat	Cost of Fuel $/Million Btu	Approximate Efficiency (%)
Electricity	28.00	100
Oil	7.00	75
Natural gas	8.00	80

8. How much will it cost to heat this house for one year if you use:

   a. electricity?

   b. oil?

   c. natural gas?

9. You investigate the cost of installing each type of heating system and find that the installation costs are $2,500 for electric heat, $6,000 for an oil system, and $5,000 for natural gas. What will be the total cost to install and operate the heating system for one year if you decide to use:

   a. electric heat?

   b. oil?

   c. natural gas?

(continued)

26. Degree-Days, Fuel, and Heating Costs *(continued)*

❑ Payback time is the time it takes to regain the money you invest in order to save money over a longer period of time. For example, let's say the cost of installing insulation in your uninsulated attic is $1,000. By insulating, however, your heating costs decrease from $1,000 to $750 per year. Your annual saving by installing insulation is $250, because:

$$\$1,000 - \$750 = \$250.$$

Your payback time is the time it will take to regain in savings the $1,000 you spent to bring about the reduced annual cost of heating your home. Therefore, your payback time is:

$$\frac{\$1,000}{\$250/\text{year}} = 4 \text{ years.}$$

However, you might have invested that money in a 4-year CD that pays 7 percent interest compounded annually. In 4 years, such an investment would be worth $1,311 because:

$$\$1,000(1.07)^4 = \$1,311.$$

Therefore, considering the possibility of such an investment, the payback time is actually 5.2 years:

$$\frac{\$1,311}{\$250/\text{year}} = 5.2 \text{ years.}$$

If you plan to stay in this home for many years, or if the cost of fuel is expected to rise dramatically in the next few years, installing insulation is probably a sound economic move. On the other hand, if you plan to move in the next year or two, it probably makes more sense to invest the $1,000 in a CD.

10. Short-term costs favor electric heat, but over a longer term, installing gas or oil heat is usually more economical. Given the information in questions 8 and 9, how long would it take before reduced fuel costs would allow you to recover the extra costs involved in installing:

    a. an oil instead of an electric heating system?

    b. a natural gas instead of an electric heating system?

27. The Usable Energy from Household Lightbulbs

When we choose a lightbulb, we generally look for the wattage rating, having decided that we want a particular wattage for a particular lamp. What does the wattage mean? Is this the best way to choose a bulb? (We will confine ourselves here to incandescent lamps.)

❑ Wattage is not simply energy. To find the amount of electrical energy required to operate a bulb, you must multiply the wattage, which measures the energy *per time*, by the time the bulb is used:

$$\frac{\text{energy}}{\text{time}} \times \text{time} = \text{energy}.$$

The energy required to operate a 100-W bulb for one hour is:

$$100\,\text{W} \times 1\ \text{hour} = 100\ \text{Watt-hour, or } 100\ \text{Wh}.$$

A kilowatt, kw, is just 1,000 W. Therefore, 100W = 0.100 kw, and 0.100 kw × 1 hour = 0.100 kilowatt-hour, or 0.100 kwh.

(We will use kilowatt-hours to measure energy because electric power companies use that unit.)

1. Obtain a bill from your electric power company. For how much electrical energy were you charged last month? What was the average cost in cents or dollars per kilowatt-hour?

❑ The usable wattage of a bulb—that is, the light energy emitted by the bulb per time—is not the same as the wattage marked on the bulb. Only a small fraction of the electrical energy is converted to light. Much of the electrical energy that enters the bulb is changed to heat, and much of the radiant energy produced is not visible light. The usable energy (light) emitted is indicated on the bulb specifications as "lumens." A lumen is simply a unit of luminous wattage. There are 683 lumens in a watt, so you can convert a bulb's lumens to watts by dividing the number of lumens by 683. For example, a 100-watt bulb that delivers 1,710 lumens of usable light delivers:

$$\frac{1{,}710\ \text{lumens}}{683\ \text{lumens/watt}} = 2.50\,\text{W}.$$

(Notice that the usable wattage—the power that appears as light—is only 2.5% of the input. This is called the efficiency.)

(continued)

27. The Usable Energy from
Household Lightbulbs *(continued)*

2. You can now prepare a table of data to show the usable luminous energy of various incandescent lightbulbs and their efficiency. You will have to go to a store that sells bulbs to find as wide a variety as possible. A supermarket is a good source. What data do you want? How will you organize your data table?

3. Which bulb gives the highest percentage of usable luminous energy?

28. Lumber and Board Feet

In the lumber business, volume is measured in board feet (bd ft). A board foot is defined as a slab of wood one foot on each side and one inch thick. The unit is used both in estimating the potential lumber in uncut trees and in the sale of lumber once it has been cut into different sizes at a sawmill.

1. How many cubic inches are there in a board foot?

2. How many cubic feet are there in a board foot?

3. Any length of lumber that measures 2 in × 4 in on its sides is called a 2 × 4 (2 by 4). At a lumberyard, you find that 2 × 4's 10 feet long cost $1.00. What is the price in $/bd ft?

4. Lumberyards make use of tables that convert various cuts of lumber of various lengths into board feet so that the customer can be charged according to the number of board feet he or she buys. The table might include 2 × 4's, 1 × 2's, 4 × 4's, 2 × 6's, 2 × 8's, and so on for lengths of 6 feet, 8 feet, and 10 feet. Prepare such a table for 2 × 4's with lengths of 6 feet, 7 feet, 8 feet, and 10 feet.

5. Why is it not necessary for tables that convert various cuts of lumber into board feet to include lengths of 12 feet, 16 feet, 18 feet, 20 feet, 24 feet, and so on?

6. A forester wants to estimate the number of board feet in a tree that may be harvested for lumber. To simplify his problem, he assumes that the tree's trunk is a cone and that it will be cut one foot above the ground. At the point at which it will be cut, it has a diameter of 4.0 feet. To find the tree's height, he stands exactly 20 feet from the base of the tree and uses an astrolabe to determine that the angle to the top of the tree at eye level is 72 degrees, as shown in Figure 5-4. (Eye level for the forester is 5.5 feet above the ground.)

(continued)

28. Lumber and Board Feet *(continued)*

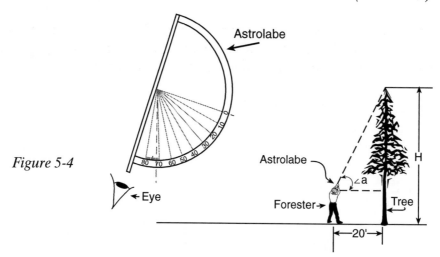

Figure 5-4

a. How does the forester determine the height of the tree, and what does he find that height to be?

b. What will be the length of the cut tree's trunk?

c. What is the volume of the cut tree's trunk, in cubic feet?

d. What is the volume of the cut tree's trunk, in board feet?

e. For trees that are to be used for pulp in the paper industry, the entire tree, bark as well as hardwood, is used. With trees that are used for lumber, the bark is stripped off. If the tree in the questions above has bark that is 2 inches thick, what volume of wood will remain after the bark is removed?

(continued)

Math You Really Need

28. Lumber and Board Feet *(continued)*

7. A log at a sawmill is 16 feet long. At its narrow end, it is 3 feet 4 inches in diameter, and the bark is 2 inches thick. The mill operator will cut the log to obtain the largest possible square cross section, as shown in Figure 5-5:

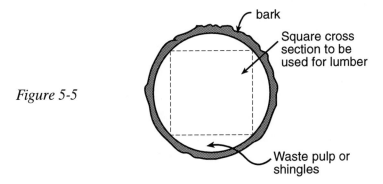

Figure 5-5

a. What will be the length of the square cross section?

b. How many board feet of lumber will be in the log after it has been "squared off" at the mill?

❏ Wood sold as fuel is measured in cords. A cord is a stack of wood 8 feet long, 4 feet high, and 4 feet deep.

8. How many cubic feet are there in a cord?

9. If wood logs were exactly the same size, an end view of the logs when stacked in cords might look like the drawing in Figure 5-6.

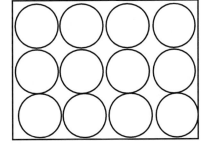

Figure 5-6

End view of stacked logs

(continued)

28. Lumber and Board Feet *(continued)*

a. If logs were stacked as shown in Figure 5-6, what fraction of the volume would be wood?

b. What fraction would be air?

c. Would you expect the actual volume of wood in a cord to be more, less, or the same as the fraction you calculated? Why?

10. Table 5-3 gives the average density, in tons per cord, and energy content, in millions of Btu per cord, of various kinds of wood.

Table 5-3: Average Density and Energy Content of Different Types of Wood

(A Btu is the amount of energy required to raise the temperature of one pound of water by one degree Fahrenheit. A million Btu is abbreviated MBtu.)

Type of Wood	Average Density (tons/cord)	Energy Content (MBtu/cord)
white oak	2.20	31.2
sugar maple	2.05	29.1
beech	2.00	28.4
yellow birch	1.90	27.0
red maple	1.70	24.1
black cherry	1.65	23.4
Douglas fir	1.45	21.5
white pine	1.10	15.8

(continued)

28. Lumber and Board Feet *(continued)*

a. The density (weight per volume) of a solid sample of white oak is found to be 52 lb/ft^3. The density of a solid sample of sugar maple is found to be 45 pounds/ft^3. Does this additional information confirm or deny your answer to question 9c? Why?

b. Plot a graph of the energy content of wood versus the density of the wood. Is there a mathematical relationship between these two variables? If there is, express that relationship in the form of an equation.

CHAPTER 6   **Math in Many Places**

To the Teacher

As the chapter's title implies, students will find they can use mathematics in many places—in estimating the number of the stars in the sky or cells in the bloodstream, in determining the height of a flagpole or the width of a river, in calculating the increased volume of the ocean due to warming, or in calculating murder rates from the number of murders and population statistics. Students with a knowledge of trigonometric functions will be able to use trig to solve some of the problems, but students can also use geometry solutions or scale drawings. Many of the problems require only arithmetic and some thought.

29, 30, & 31. *Estimation and Approximation* (pages 133–138)

We begin this chapter with three examples of how estimates and approximations are made. The first section, "How Many Stars in the Night Sky?" is not really an example of the everyday use of mathematics, but it is almost certain to be of interest to students. We can't count the stars, one by one, but we can estimate their number fairly easily with some geometric ideas.

The second example, "Approximating Distance," is about as useful an example of everyday math as one can find.

The third example, "Sampling Red Blood Cells," demonstrates an estimating technique that can be used to "count" red blood cells. The procedures shown here are typical of those used in other areas of science, social science, and technology.

It is of great importance to discuss in class the limits of estimation. Have the students come up with other examples of things that can be usefully estimated, and be sure to have them point out examples where an estimate is *not* sufficient. You can use the ideas presented in the Chapter 2 activity "MPG, the EPA, and the Cost of Driving" to illustrate this point. The EPA estimates of mpg found in that activity are useful for comparing cars, but you had better know the real mpg for your own car if you're driving a long distance through the desert.

29. How Many Stars in the Night Sky? *(page 133)*

Answers

1. Answers will vary because of factors such as area of the sky sampled, haze, and light pollution near cities. A typical series of counts might be 60, 55, 66, 70, 57.

2. Answers will vary depending on counts given in question 1. The average star count for the numbers in question 1 is 62.

3. The surface area of the hemisphere is given by:

$$S = \frac{4\pi r^2}{2} = \frac{4\pi 30^2}{2} = 5,655 \text{ cm}^2.$$

4. The area of the cutout is $\pi r^2 = \pi 6^2 = 113 \text{ cm}^2$.

5. $113/5,655 = 0.02$ of the area of the hemisphere

6. We have viewed 0.02 of the night sky.

7. We have counted 0.02 of the visible stars.

8. The number of visible stars in the night sky is $62 \times 100/2 = 3,100$.

9. The class averages should be similar to the above data.

10. An astronomer will take a photograph of a galaxy or will have a computer-enhanced image. The telescope will have been calibrated so that the fraction of the galactic area occupied by any specific small area of the galaxy is known. Then the stars in the small area are counted. Their density (stars per area) provides a standard from which the densities of all the other areas making up the galaxy can be referenced. A computer is used to scan the surface area of the galaxy, measuring the densities of each small area. From the densities, the number of stars is summarized.

30. Approximating Distance *(page 135)*

Answers

1. A typical pace will average about 5 feet.

2. Multiplying the number of paces by the feet per pace will give the distance.

3. A baseball diamond is really a square, 90 feet × 90 feet. Thus the area is 8,100 square feet. The area of an entire field will vary.

31. Sampling Red Blood Cells *(page 136)*

In this set of questions students see an example of how estimating can be used to count red blood cells. It can also be used to emphasize the importance of scientific notation (see Skill-Builder 2 on page *xii*) in problems that involve large (number of red blood cells) and small (size of red blood cells) numbers. In addition to problems 1–3 related to estimating the number of cells, seven supplementary problems (problems 4–10) not directly related to the estimation of red blood cells in the body are provided in this activity if you wish to use them. We believe many students will find them interesting, particularly if the students are studying biology.

Answers

1. $450 \times 10{,}000 = 4{,}500{,}000$ rbc/mm^3

2. 4.5×10^6 rbc/mm$^3 \times 1{,}000$ mm^3/cm$^3 \times 1{,}000$ cm^3/L $\times 5.0$ L $= 2.3 \times 10^{13}$ rbc

3. $1.3 \times 4{,}500{,}000$ rbc/mm$^3 = 5{,}900{,}000$ rbc/mm^3 or $1.3 \times 2.3 \times 10^{13}$ rbc $= 3.0 \times 10^{13}$ rbc

4. a. Volume $= \pi r^2 h = \dfrac{\pi d^2}{4} \times h = \dfrac{\pi \times 7.7^2}{4} \times 1.9 = 88 \ \mu^3$

   b. $88 \ \mu^3 \times \dfrac{1 m^3}{1.0 \times 10^{18} \mu^3}$ on $\dfrac{1.0 \times 10^{-18} m^3}{\mu^3} = 8.8 \times 10^{-17}$ m^3

5. The volume of a red blood cell (rbc) in liters is:

   8.8×10^{-17} m^3/rbc $\times 1.0 \times 10^3$ L/m$^3 = 8.8 \times 10^{-14}$ L/rbc. The total volume of rbc in the human body is: 2.3×10^{13} rbc $\times 8.8 \times 10^{-14}$ L/rbc $= 2.0$ L. Thus, the fraction of the blood that is made up of rbc is: 2.0 L/5.0 L $= 0.40$.

6. a. Assuming the red blood cells to be cylinders: area $= 2\pi r^2 + 2\pi rh = 2\pi r(r + h) = 2\pi \times 7.7 \ \mu/2(7.7 \ \mu/2 + 1.9 \ \mu) = 93 \ \mu^2 + 46 \ \mu^2 = 140 \ \mu^2$.

   b. $140 \ \mu^2 \times 1.0 \times 10^{-12}$ m^2/$\mu^2 = 1.4 \times 10^{-10}$ m^2

7. Total surface area $= 1.4 \times 10^{-10}$ m^2/rbc $\times 2.3 \times 10^{13}$ rbc $= 3.2 \times 10^3$ m^2; an area about 3/4 that of a football field.

8. Red blood cells carry oxygen from the lungs to all the cells of the body. It is through the surface of these cells that oxygen enters and leaves. A rapid transfer of the gas into and out of the cells requires a large surface area.

9. Circumference of the earth $= \pi d = \pi \times 12.8 \times 10^6$ m $= 4.0 \times 10^7$ m.
   $\dfrac{2.3 \times 10^{13} \text{rbc} \times 7.7 \times 10^{-6} \text{ m/rbc}}{4.0 \times 10^7 \text{ m}} = 4.4$ times.

10. a. Weight of blood $= 250$ lb $\times 1/15 = 17$ lb. Volume of blood $=$
    $\dfrac{17 \text{ lb}}{1.05 \times 2.2 \text{ lb/L}} = 7.4$ L

    b. Weight of 5.0 L of blood $= 5.0$ L $\times 1.05 \times 2.2$ lb/L $= 12$ lb. Let $X =$ average weight of person with 12 lb of blood: $1/15 \ X = 12$ lb; $X = 12$ lb $\times 15 = 180$ lb.

    c. Most people will probably think 180 pounds is an above-average weight.

    d. Answers will vary, because average weight depends on age and sex. Assuming 140 pounds as an average, we would expect the average blood volume to be: $\dfrac{140 \text{ lb} \times 1/15}{1.05 \times 2.2 \text{ lb/L}} = 4.0$ L.

32. Flagpole Math *(page 139)*

The purpose of the question raised here is to encourage students to use their imagination as well as their knowledge of mathematics to determine the height of something they cannot measure directly. A knowledge of trigonometry is helpful but not essential. Scale drawings can be used and may in fact be suggested by students who have not studied simple trigonometric functions.

For students who know basic trigonometric functions, this section and the next ("How Wide Is the River?") provide an opportunity for them to apply trigonometry to practical problems as recommended by the NCTM standards.

Answers

Here are some of the possible methods that students might suggest.

1. Measure the length of their shadow or the shadow of a vertical stick of known length and the length of the flagpole's shadow. Then, using the proportion $X/S_{fp} = H_s/S_s$, where X is the height of the flagpole, S_{fp} is the length of the flagpole's shadow, H_s is the height of the stick or person, and S_s is the length of the stick's or the person's shadow, the equation can be solved for X. (See Figure T 6-1.)

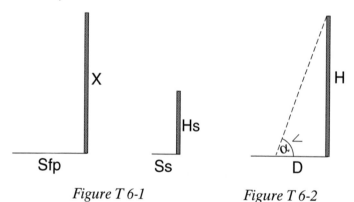

Figure T 6-1   *Figure T 6-2*

2. Pull the rope of the flagpole out and bring it to the ground as shown in Figure T 6-2. Measure the the angle between the ground and the rope. Then the ratio of the height of the flagpole, H, to the distance from the end of the rope to the pole, D, will equal the tangent of the angle (α). Therefore, $\tan \alpha = H/D$; so $H = D \tan \alpha$. Any additional height from the top of the rope to the top of the pole can be estimated.

3. Use an astrolabe or transit to measure the angle to the top of the pole at a known distance from its base. Then use the tangent of the angle to find the height. In this case, the height will be from the position at which the top is sighted; consequently, the sighting height will have to be added to the height calculated.

33. How Wide Is the River? *(page 140)*

You might begin this section by giving small groups of students question 1 and the information that precedes it to see if they can develop a satisfactory method for finding the width of the river using their knowledge of geometry and/or trigonometry. You can then give them the approach used by the engineer (question 2) and let them finish her work in whatever way they can. In question 3, all the measurements are given. Students can use the data to calculate the width of the river.

Answers

1. Answers will vary. Students with a knowledge of trigonometry or geometry may suggest establishing sight lines and perpendiculars similar to those shown in Figure 6-4 so that either similar triangles can be established for a geometric solution, or known sides can be measured to establish an angle so that trigonometric functions can be used. Students without an understanding of either geometry or trigonometry will probably suggest making scale drawings.

2. Students who were unable to suggest a method may fare better now that they have the lines laid out by the engineer in Figure 6-4.

3. She can use similar triangles, because the small triangle at the right side of the drawing and the large triangle, which includes the width of the river within X_0X_2, are similar. Both are right triangles, and they share a common angle $X_5X_4X_6$. Consequently:

   $a/X_4X_6 = X_0X_2/X_2X_4$; $X_0X_2 = a \times X_2X_4/X_4X_6 = 85$ yd $\times$ 220 yd/81 yd = 231 yd. The width of the river = 231 yd – b = 231 yd – 91 yd = 140 yd.

   She might also use trigonometry, because the tangent of angle $X_5X_4X_6$ is the ratio of side a to side X_4X_6. Tan $X_5X_4X_6 = a/X_4X_6 = 85/81 = 1.05$. Therefore, $X_0X_2/X_2X_4 = 1.05$, and $X_0X_2 = 1.05 \times X_2X_4 = 1.05 \times 220$ yd = 231 yd; 231 yd – 91 yd = 140 yd.

4. From the Pythagorean theorem, $a^2 + X_4X_6^2 =$ hypotenuse^2, hypotenuse$^2 = (85$ yd$)^2 + (81$ yd$)^2 = 13,800$ yd^2; hypotenuse = 117 yd.

34. Rising Seas *(page 142)*

This section is based on data from the TOPEX/Poseidon satellite, which was launched in 1992. The information collected by the satellite indicates that ocean levels rose about 3 mm per year between 1992 and 1995. Students are asked to make the assumption that the increase came from the expansion of water due to an increase in the water's temperature. Of course, some of the water's increased volume may be melt water from the earth's glaciers as well, which you might like to bring to your students' attention. This could serve as a lead into a discussion of what additional information would be needed to assess glacier melting.

The use of scientific notation and significant figures would be useful here. For more information and practice problems regarding scientific notation and significant figures, see Skill-Builders 2 and 3 on pages *xii* and *xv*, respectively..

Answers

1. a. $C = \pi d$; $d = C/\pi = 7,926$ mi

    b. $r = d/2 = 3,963$ mi

2. Area of earth = $4\pi r^2 = 4\pi \times (3,963 \text{ mi})^2 = 197,000,000 \ (1.97 \times 10^8) \text{ mi}^2$.
    Area of earth's oceans = $0.71 \times 197,000,000 \ (1.97 \times 10^8) \text{ mi}^2 = 140,000,000 \ (1.4 \times 10^8) \text{ mi}^2$.

3. Volume = area × depth = $140,000,000 \ (1.4 \times 10^8) \text{ mi}^2 \times \dfrac{12,000 \text{ ft}}{5,280 \text{ ft/mi}}$
    $= 320,000,000 \ (3.2 \times 10^8) \text{ mi}^3$

4. Increased depth, in miles = $0.3 \text{ cm} \times \dfrac{1 \text{ in}}{2.54 \text{ cm}} \times \dfrac{1.0 \text{ ft}}{12 \text{ in}} \times \dfrac{1.0 \text{ mi}}{5,280 \text{ ft}} = 0.0000019$ mi, or 1.9×10^{-6} mi.

    Increased volume = $1.9 \times 10^{-6} \text{ mi} \times 1.4 \times 10^8 \text{ mi}^2 = 2.7 \times 10^2$, or 270 mi^3.

5. The fractional expansion of the earth's water = $270 \text{ mi}^3/320,000,000 \text{ mi}^3 = 0.00000084$, or 8.4×10^{-7}. A rise of 1°C would cause a fractional increase of 0.00036, or 3.6×10^{-4}; $8.4 \times 10^{-7}/3.6 \times 10^{-4}/°C = 2.3 \times 10^{-3}°C$, or $0.0023°C$.

    This is equivalent to 0.004°F.

6. $0.3 \text{ cm} \times \dfrac{1 \text{ in}}{2.54 \text{ cm}} \times \dfrac{1.0 \text{ ft}}{12 \text{ in}} = 0.0098 \text{ ft}$; $0.0098 \text{ ft}/12,000 \text{ ft} = 8.2 \times 10^{-7}$.

    This is very nearly the same as the fractional increase in volume. The results should be the same. The increase in volume arises because of an increase in depth. Assuming the oceans' areas remain unchanged, the increased volume must arise from an increase in depth.

35. *Statistics, Lies, and Murders* (page 143)

Blindly applying rules involving simple algebra and proportions to attain statistical data can produce misleading information, as the example taken from real-world numbers reveals. After seeing the problem that arises when small numbers are used to arrive at statistical data, students are asked to suggest ways of using the data so that misconceptions could be avoided.

In question 4, students examine the nation's murder rate and its growing population from 1975 to 1992 and beyond. In question 5, they compare murder rates in two large cities—New York and London.

Answers

1. $\dfrac{x}{100{,}000 \text{ residents}} = \dfrac{1 \text{ murder}}{2{,}491 \text{ residents}}$; $x = \dfrac{1 \text{ murder} \times 100{,}000 \text{ residents}}{2{,}491 \text{ residents}}$;

   $x = 40$ murders

2. $\dfrac{17 \text{ murders}}{100{,}000 \text{ residents}} = \dfrac{98 \text{ murders}}{x}$; $x = \dfrac{98 \text{ murders} \times 100{,}000 \text{ residents}}{17 \text{ murders}}$;

   $x = 576{,}000$ residents.

3. a. Answers will vary, but in general, they should indicate that with small populations, a single murder can produce a statistic that grossly overstates the crime rate in the community.

   b. Answers will vary. One approach might be to take the total number of murders over a period of many years per the average population over those years times the number of years. For example, if there had been one murder in Wellfleet in 50 years and the average population over those years had been 1,000 people, the murder rate might be reported as:

   $$\dfrac{1.0 \text{ murder}}{1{,}000 \text{ residents/yr} \times 50 \text{ yr}} = \dfrac{x}{100{,}000 \text{ residents}}; \; x = 2 \text{ murders.}$$

   c. Probably not. The statistics for cities, which are based on a much larger sample, are useful in seeing what is happening to the crime rate over a period of several years as various attempts to reduce crime are put in place.

4. a.

Year	Population	Murders	Murders per 100,000	Year	Population	Murders	Murders per 100,000
1975	213,124,000	20,510	9.6	1984	236,158,000	18,690	7.9
1976	214,659,000	18,780	8.7	1985	238,740,000	18,980	8.0
1977	216,332,000	19,120	8.8	1986	241,077,000	20,610	8.5
1978	218,059,000	19,560	9.0	1987	243,400,000	20,100	8.3
1979	220,099,000	21,460	9.8	1988	245,807,000	20,680	8.4
1980	225,349,000	23,040	10.2	1989	248,239,000	21,500	8.7
1981	229,146,000	22,520	9.8	1990	248,710,000	23,440	9.4
1982	231,534,000	21,010	9.1	1991	252,177,000	24,700	9.8
1983	233,981,000	19,310	8.3	1992	255,082,000	23,760	9.3

   b. $255{,}082{,}000 - 213{,}124{,}000 = 41{,}958{,}000$; $\dfrac{41{,}958{,}000}{213{,}124{,}000} \times 100 = 19.7\%$

   c. $23{,}760 - 20{,}510 = 3{,}250$; $\dfrac{3{,}250}{20{,}510} \times 100 = 15.8\%$

   d. The percentage increase in murders is less than the percentage increase in the population.

e. The graph should resemble Figure T 6-4. It reveals that the murder rate fluctuates between about 8 and 10 per 100,000.

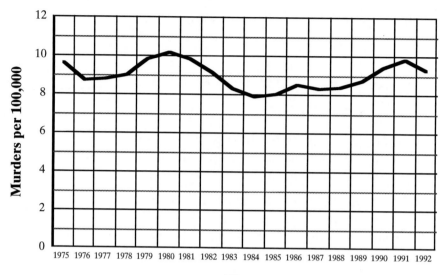

Year

Figure T 6-4

f. The data reveal that in many years the total number of murders actually decreases; however, in general, the number of murders that take place each year does increase as the population grows. The rate of murders in murders per 100,000 people seems to fluctuate. From 1976 to 1980, the murder rate increased. It then decreased between 1980 and 1984, only to climb again, level off, and then rise to another peak in 1991.

g. Answers will vary depending on the new figures students find.

5. a. Murder rate in murders/100,000:

New York: $\dfrac{1.995 \times 10^3}{7.3 \times 10^6} \times \dfrac{x}{1.0 \times 10^5}$; $x = \dfrac{(1.995 \times 10^3) \times (1.0 \times 10^5)}{(7.3 \times 10^6)} = 27$

London: $\dfrac{185}{6.8 \times 10^6} = \dfrac{x}{1.0 \times 10^5}$; $x = \dfrac{185 \times (1.0 \times 10^5)}{6.8 \times 10^6} = 2.7$

b. Answers will vary, but one major reason is that most English citizens are not allowed to own guns.

29. Estimation and Approximation: How Many Stars in the Night Sky?

When should we estimate a measurement or a calculation? When should we be "exact," and just what does "exact" mean?

Here is a typical situation. Suppose you would like to find the number of stars visible in the sky. Obviously this will have to be an estimate or approximation. But is it possible to estimate this number? Can an approximation be made without actually getting on a high piece of ground where you can see a complete horizon and then counting the stars? But certainly you won't be able to count them one by one.

You can do this activity alone or as a class project. If done as a class project, each student can collect data and the data can be shared by the class. The class results can then be compared.

Figure 6-1 shows you the basic idea of this experiment.

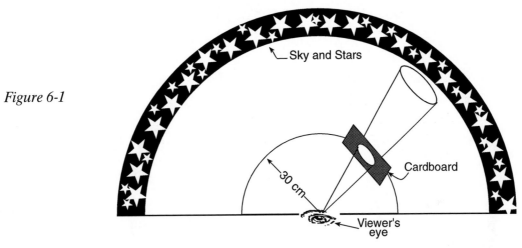

Figure 6-1

A circular window has been cut out of a piece of cardboard. The diameter of the circle is 12 cm. On a clear, moonless night, hold the window 30 cm from your eyes.

1. Count and record the number of stars that are visible when viewed through the circular cutout held at 30 cm. Repeat this count a number of times, viewing the stars at differing angles, but don't include the Milky Way.

2. What is the average star count from all your measurements?

(continued)

29. Estimation and Approximation: How Many Stars in the Night Sky? *(continued)*

3. From the drawing, you can see that the circular cutout lies on a hemisphere of radius 30 cm. The surface area of a complete sphere is given by $4\pi r^2$. What is the surface area of this hemisphere?

4. What is the area of the circular cutout?

5. What fraction of the total area of the hemisphere is the area of the cutout?

6. What fraction of the night sky do you view through the cutout?

7. What fraction of the visible stars do you see through the cutout?

8. What is your estimate of the number of stars visible in the night sky?

9. If appropriate, compare your results with those of your classmates. What is the class estimate of the number of stars visible in the night sky?

10. Describe how astronomers estimate the number of stars in a galaxy.

Math You Really Need

30. Estimation and Approximation: Approximating Distance

It is very useful to be able to approximate a distance. Suppose you want to measure off a baseball diamond for a pickup game or would like to know the distance from one telephone pole to another. You don't need these measurements to the nearest inch, but you would like them to the nearest foot. You can easily get the answers if you know the length of your pace. A pace is sketched in Figure 6-2.

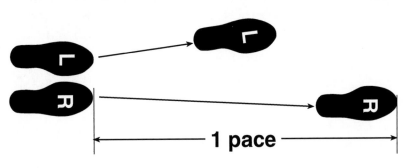

1 pace

Figure 6-2

1. Every time your right foot goes down, you have covered another pace. From the distance you cover in 100 paces, find the average length of one pace. This is a number that can be of use to you dozens of times over as the years go by.

2. Now find the number of paces that will take you from one block to the next, or from one lamp pole to the next. Knowing the length of one of your paces, find the distance in feet from block to block, or from pole to pole.

3. Find the area of a baseball field using paces to measure lengths.

31. Estimation and Approximation: Sampling Red Blood Cells

Suppose you need to know the number of objects in a container that is too large to allow you to count individually. You can first sample a small measurable volume and count the objects. Then find the volume of the large container and you'll be able to find the total number of objects.

For example, suppose that we want to know the number of beans in a large jar that measures 50 cm across its circular base and stands 150 cm high. We remove a small sample to a 500-cubic-centimeter beaker and count 378 beans in the beaker. That means that there are $2 \times 378 = 756$ beans in every 1,000 cm^3. The volume of the large vessel is the volume of a cylinder of radius 25 cm and height 150 cm:

Volume $= \pi r^2 h = 3.14 \times (25\text{cm})^2 \times 150 \text{ cm} = 294,375 \text{ cm}^3$.

Since every 1,000 cm^3 contains 756 beans, there are $294.4 \times 756 \approx 223,000$ beans in the large container.

A drop of blood when spread out on a glass slide and viewed through a microscope reveals a vast number of tiny dumbbell-shaped cells. These cells are red blood cells. They are the cells that carry oxygen from our lungs to the other cells of our bodies. One look through the microscope would convince you that it would be not only tedious but also impossible to count all the red blood cells in your body. When a blood test reports a red blood cell count of so many million per cubic millimeter, it is based on an estimate made by a laboratory technician.

To make such an estimate, a technician can draw a tiny volume of a patient's blood into a small pipette. The blood is diluted by mixing one part blood with 199 parts saline (salt) solution. After the blood and saline are thoroughly mixed, a drop of the diluted blood is placed in a small, shallow counting chamber that has a volume of exactly 0.10 cubic millimeter. The chamber is divided by cross-rulings into 400 equal spaces. The technician then looks at the diluted blood in the chamber through a microscope and counts the number of red blood cells in 80 of the 400 spaces.

❑ Let's assume that the technician counts a total of 450 red blood cells in the 80 spaces. How does he or she then estimate the number of red blood cells per cubic millimeter?

The technician counted the cells in 80 of the 400 cells, or 80/400 of the the cells in the chamber. Since 80/400 = 1/5, only 20 percent of the cells were actually counted. To estimate the total number of red blood cells in the chamber, we would have to multiply the number actually counted by 5. But the volume of the chamber was only 0.10 mm^3. To estimate the total number of cells in one cubic millimeter of the diluted blood, the technician would have to multiply by 10, since the chamber was only 1/10 mm^3. So far,

(continued)

31. Estimation and Approximation:
Sampling Red Blood Cells *(continued)*

the number of cells counted has been multiplied by 50 (5×10). But remember, the blood was diluted 1:200 when it was mixed with saline solution. Consequently, to make an accurate estimate, the technician would have to multiply again by 200. Altogether then, the number of cells actually counted would have to be multiplied by $5 \times 10 \times 200 = 10{,}000$ to estimate the number of red blood cells in 1.0 mm^3 of blood.

1. What number would the technician record as the number of red blood cells per cubic millimeter for the sample of blood described above?

2. The volume of blood in the average adult is about 5.0 liters. Estimate the total number of red blood cells in the body of the person from whom the sample described above was taken.

3. Sustained living at altitudes of 10,000 feet or higher leads to an increase of about 30 percent in the number of red blood cells found in a person's blood. Assuming the person described in the sample blood count above were to move to a town 11,000 feet above sea level, what might you expect to find his or her red blood cell count to be after a year?

4. Red blood cells are donut-shaped. From the side, they have a slightly dumbbell appearance as shown in Figure 6-3.

Figure 6-3

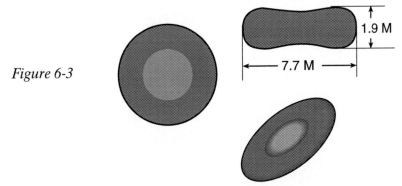

For purposes of approximation, they can be regarded as flat cylinders with an average diameter of 7.7 microns (7.7×10^{-6} m) and a thickness of 1.9 microns. What is the approximate volume of a red blood cell in:

a. cubic microns?

b. cubic meters?

(continued)

31. Estimation and Approximation:
Sampling Red Blood Cells *(continued)*

5. Approximately what fraction of the volume of human blood consists of red blood cells?

6. Estimate the surface area of a red blood cell in:

   a. square microns.

   b. square meters.

7. Estimate the total surface area of all the red blood cells in the human bloodstream.

8. Why is it important that the total surface area of red blood cells be so large?

9. If all the red blood cells in the blood of an average human being were lined up side by side, how many times would they encircle the earth?

10. Blood constitutes about 7 percent of a person's weight, and it has a specific gravity of about 1.05, which means that it weighs 1.05 times as much as an equal volume of water. The density of the human body is about the same as water— 1.0 kg/L, or 2.2 pounds per liter.

    a. What volume of blood would you expect a 250-pound football player to have?

    b. We assumed that an average person has about 5.0 liters of blood. What weight did we assume our average person to have?

    c. Do you think the weight of our average person was too heavy, too light, or about right?

    d. Choose what you think the average human weight is, and then calculate what you would expect the average blood volume to be.

32. Flagpole Math

You are challenged to find the height of a flagpole on a village green without attempting to climb to the top.

1. Use your knowledge of mathematics to suggest several ways that this might be done.

       Math You Really Need

33. How Wide Is the River?

An engineer involved in a preliminary study to evaluate the cost of building a bridge across a swift-flowing river decides that she needs to begin by making a rough determination of the river's width. Available are some sticks, string, a hammer, a tape measure, and an engineer's pocket calculator.

1. Using your knowledge of mathematics and the materials available, develop a method for determining the width of the river.

2. The engineer decides to establish a sight line straight across the river by aligning several sticks (X_1, X_2, and X_3) on her side of the river with an object, X_0, close to the shore on the other side of the river as shown in Figure 6-4.

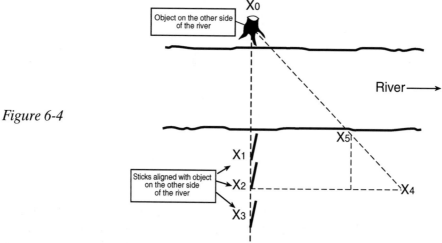

Figure 6-4

At X_2, she constructs a line (X_2X_4) perpendicular to line $X_1X_2X_3$. At X_4, she constructs a second sight line (X_4X_5) to the object X_0 on the other side of the river. Suggest several different ways the engineer can now determine the width of the river.

(continued)

Math You Really Need

33. How Wide Is the River? *(continued)*

3. At X_6, the engineer constructs a line perpendicular to X_2X_4 and extends it to the sight line X_4X_5 as shown in Figure 6-5.

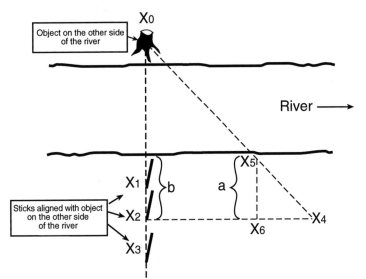

Figure 6-5

She then uses the tape measure to determine some distances. She finds that X_4X_6 is 81 yards long, X_2X_4 is 220 yards long, the perpendicular distance from X_6 to the sight line X_4X_5 (*a* in the drawing) is 85 yards, and the distance from $X2$ to the river (*b* in the drawing) is 91 yards. From her measurements, how does she determine the width of the river? What does she find the width of the river to be?

4. To be certain that line *a* is perpendicular to X_2X_4, the engineer measures the distance from X_4 to the intersection of line *a* with sight line X_4X_0. If *a* is perpendicular to X_2X_4, what should her measurement be?

34. Rising Seas

Data from the TOPEX/Poseidon satellite, which was launched in 1992, indicate that ocean levels rose about 3 mm per year between 1992 and 1995. The rise may indicate a general global warming that is causing glaciers to melt and seawater to expand. You can use these data together with additional data about the earth and water to make rough estimates of how much the average temperature has risen.

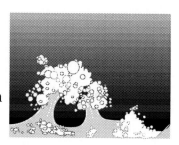

❑ The average depth of the world's oceans and seas = 12,000 feet.

❑ Fraction of the earth's surface covered by oceans and seas = 71%.

❑ Earth's circumference = 24,900 miles.

❑ At the ocean's average temperature, water expands by about 3.6×10^{-4} (0.00036) of its volume for each increase of 1°C.

1. If the earth's circumference is 24,900 miles, what is its:

   a. diameter?

   b. radius?

2. What is the area of the earth's oceans?

3. What is the approximate volume of the earth's oceans?

4. If the oceans are rising 3 mm each year, by what volume, in cubic miles, are they increasing each year?

5. Assuming that the ocean's rising level is caused solely by the expansion of water brought about by an increase in its temperature, by how much is the ocean's temperature increasing each year according to the data given here?

6. Compare the fractional increase of the ocean's volume with the fractional increase in its depth brought about by a rise of 3 mm. Explain your comparison.

35. Statistics, Lies, and Murders

A newspaper story reported that Wellfleet, a small town in Massachusetts, had the highest murder rate in the state during 1993—nearly two and a half times the murder rate in Boston, the state's largest city. Police officials in Wellfleet could not remember a single murder that took place in that town in 1993. In fact, a police lieutenant who had lived in the town for nearly 50 years said he could not remember a single murder that had taken place in the town during all those years.

However, in 1993, a murder suspect from a larger town had turned himself in to Wellfleet police, who were credited with the arrest. The murder was, therefore, recorded as having occurred in the town where the arrest was made. But even if the murder had taken place in Wellfleet, the following problems will help you to see how a method of calculating murder rates can make a small, peaceful, rural town appear to be the murder capital of a state.

1. In 1993, Wellfleet had a population of 2,491 residents. Murder rate statistics for cities and towns are based on murders per 100,000 residents. If there had been a murder in Wellfleet in 1993, what would have been the murder rate statistic in murders per 100,000 residents?

2. In 1993, the murder rate in Boston was 17 per 100,000 residents, and there were 98 murders. According to these statistics, what was Boston's population in 1993?

3. a. Why does the method of presenting murder rates in murders per 100,000 residents sometimes give results that do not reflect the true nature of crime in a community?

   b. How might the statistic be reported so as to give a more accurate representation of crime in a town?

(continued)

35. Statistics, Lies, and Murders *(continued)*

c. Would such a method be appropriate for large cities?

4. Table 6-1 provides information about the U.S. population and the number of murders committed in the country from 1975 to 1992.

Table 6-1: Population of U.S. and Murders Committed from 1975 to 1992

Year	Population	Murders	Murders per 100,000	Year	Population	Murders	Murders per 100,000
1975	213,124,000	20,510		1984	236,158,000	18,690	
1976	214,659,000	18,780		1985	238,740,000	18,980	
1977	216,332,000	19,120		1986	241,077,000	20,610	
1978	218,059,000	19,560		1987	243,400,000	20,100	
1979	220,099,000	21,460		1988	245,807,000	20,680	
1980	225,349,000	23,040		1989	248,239,000	21,500	
1981	229,146,000	22,520		1990	248,710,000	23,440	
1982	231,534,000	21,010		1991	252,177,000	24,700	
1983	233,981,000	19,310		1992	255,082,000	23,760	

Source: Uniform Crime Reports, FBI

a. Calculate the murder rate for each year in murders per 100,000 citizens. Record the rates in the columns labeled "Murders per 100,000."

b. What was the percentage increase in the U.S. population between 1975 and 1992?

c. What was the percentage increase in murders between 1975 and 1992?

d. How does the percentage increase in the population between 1975 and 1992 compare with the percentage increase in murders committed during the same period?

(continued)

35. Statistics, Lies, and Murders *(continued)*

e. Plot a graph of the murder rate in murders/100,000 citizens as a function of time in years from 1975 to 1992. What can you conclude from the graph you have plotted?

f. We often hear or read that the number of murders is increasing each year. We hear, too, that murder rates are constantly increasing. Based on the data you have seen in this question, what do you conclude?

g. Consult a new almanac and find out what has happened to the murder rate and the total number of murders between 1992 and the latest figures you can find.

5. The population of New York City is about 7.3 million. The population of London, England, is about 6.8 million. In 1991, there were 1,995 murders in New York City and 185 in London.

   a. What was the murder rate, in murders/100,000 citizens, in New York? in London?

   b. How can you account for the difference in crime rate between these two cities?

          Math You Really Need